Theory of Vibrations

N. W. McLachlan, D. Sc.

DOVER PUBLICATIONS, INC.

THE DOVER SERIES IN MATHEMATICS AND PHYSICS

W. PRAGER, *Consulting Editor*

Contents

Contents

Preface

This book is intended to serve as a short, concise, analytical text for a first semester graduate course. It is based upon lectures given by the Author in the Graduate Division of Applied Mathematics, while visiting Professor at Brown University, Providence, R. I. Owing to limitation in length, practical applications, exercises, and additional matter given in the lectures, have had to be omitted. These, however, would be supplied by the lecturer in any case. It has been necessary to assume that the reader has an elementary working knowledge of Bessel functions, Fourier's integral theorem, and Operational Calculus. Such knowledge may *now* be regarded as a pre-requisite for the analytical study of vibrational problems. The Chapters proceed in logical sequence, and as far as possible (apart from starred sections, which are intended for a second reading), in order of analytical difficulty.

Symbols and abbreviations. In general these are standard, but heavy type has been used to signify 'per unit length', 'per unit area', and the moment of inertia of a disk, normal type representing that for a cross-section. The symbol $\Rightarrow$ has been used to signify the p-multiplied Laplace transform. It was introduced by the Author in 1938, and is now standard in France. Being made with one motion of the pen, it is much simpler than any other notation yet proposed. A slight modification of the symbol for use with the *ordinary* L.T. will be found in reference [13] p. 23.

$f(t) \Rightarrow \phi(p)$ means that $\phi(p)$ is the p-multiplied Laplace transform of $f(t)$,

$\simeq$ means   is approximately equal to,

$\sim$ means   is analogous to,

[ ]   means   an item in the list of references,

b.c.	means	boundary condition,
c.f.	means	complementary function,
c-s	means	cross-sectional,
d.d.c.	means	dynamic deformation curve,
D.E.	means	differential equation,
e.m.f.	means	electromotive force,
K.E.	means	kinetic energy,
l.h.s.	means	left hand side,
L.T.	means	p-multiplied Laplace transform,
m.o.i.	means	moment of inertia,
p.d.(s)	means	potential difference(s),
p.i.	means	particular integral,
r.h.s.	means	right hand side.

N.W.M.

CHAPTER I

Linear Systems having One Degree of Freedom

1. **INTRODUCTION** Vibration is ubiquitous! It occurs in every phase of life. The human body cannot survive without the beating of the heart, while speech or any mode of transportation, even the act of walking, is associated with vibration. Most vibrations are complicated, e.g. those of an automobile on a rough road. By aid of mathematical analysis based upon suitable assumptions, complicated vibrations may be split up into simple types, just as a periodic function, an alternating current, or a continuous sound wave, may be analysed into its Fourier components. To obtain a solution adequate to account for the behaviour of an intricate system, often depends largely on the skill with which the basic simplifying assumptions are made. This is especially the case if numerical values computed from the analysis have to be compared with observed data. Otherwise the assumptions may be less rigorous, e.g. when a purely qualitative description of a physical phenomenon is needed.

A vibrational system is essentially one having mass and stiffness, or their analogs. Stiffness implies that alteration in the configuration due to an applied force is accompanied by a change in potential energy (strain). Tension in a string is equivalent to stiffness of a bar.

The electrical analogs of mass and stiffness are inductance and elastance (reciprocal of capacitance). Alternatively, compliance (reciprocal of stiffness) and capacitance are analogous. Theoretically it is expedient, in certain cases, to consider 'idealised' or pure masses and stiffnesses, or their analogs. The vibrating system is then said to be 'discrete' in type. Examples are a relatively heavy mass vibrating on a coil spring, or the balance wheel and hair spring of a watch. Such systems, in which the motion is specified by only *one* coordinate,* are said to have *one degree of freedom*. In §70 the velocity c of a disturbance along the spring is $(s/m)^{1/2}$, so when the spring has stiffness only, the mass is zero and c infinite. Thus a force applied at one end of the spring is communicated to the other end instantaneously, so the spring moves in phase throughout. This result is approximated by a spring and a relatively large mass, but since no *actual* velocity can exceed that of light, the 'idealised' spring must be regarded as a convenient fiction!

When the mass and stiffness (or their analogs) are *distributed*, either uniformly or non-uniformly without a break, the system is said to be *continuous*, e.g. a violin string, the skin of a kettledrum. In a rigorous sense all systems are continuous, for each element of a discrete system may be set into vibration independently. The pendulum of a clock may be regarded as a discrete vibrational system, whose frequency is sub-sonic. But if we remove the bob and tap either it or the pendulum rod, audible vibrations ensue. Thus each element of the discrete system is itself a continuous system, but the lowest frequencies of the latter far exceed in value that of the (idealised) discrete system which they represent jointly in practice. Moreover, in general a discrete system is one composed of continuous elements, whose lowest free frequencies are much greater than those of the composite system. The same argument is applicable to electrical circuits comprising inductance, capacitance, and resistance. In practice, every coil has capacitance and resistance, and free electrical oscillations may occur if the resistance is not too high, i.e. the system is a continuous type. But by connecting a relatively large capacitance in parallel with the coil, the system may be regarded as discrete. The frequency of the combination is now a small fraction of the fundamental of the coil alone. The current is substantially in phase throughout the circuit, which has one degree of freedom, since only one coordinate (current) is needed to describe the (analogous) motion completely. Moreover, there is no such physical quantity as a *pure* mass. stiffness, inductance, capacitance, or resistance.

---

*x for the mass, and θ for the wheel.

But from an analytical viewpoint, provided certain conditions are satisfied, it is expedient to consider each of these to exist separately.

2. SIMPLE MASS-SPRING SYSTEM   Fig. 2.1A is a schematic diagram for a discrete mechanical system, where a mass m is fixed to a uniform helical spring s, whose other end is anchored. If m is displaced from its central or equilibrium position (when at rest), it will execute oscillations about that position. The motion is specified completely by one coordinate x, so the system has one degree of freedom.* To simplify the mathe-

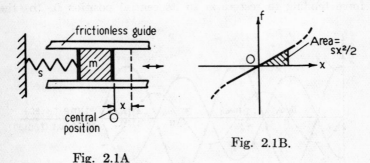

Fig. 2.1A

Fig. 2.1B.

matical analysis, we assume that (a) there is absence of loss, i.e. the motion is undamped, (b) the mass of the spring $m_s \ll m$. If the spring is loaded by known static forces, and the corresponding displacements measured, the graphical relationship between them is illustrated in Fig. 2.1B. This is the force-displacement 'characteristic' of the system, being linear provided the displacement is within certain limits. Beyond these, the graph takes the non-linear form indicated by the broken lines. We shall confine our attention to the linear part of the graph where the relationship is $f = sx$, s being the force per unit axial displacement ($\pm$), or the 'stiffness' of the *complete*

---

*A mass and spring without the guides shown in Fig. 2.1A has several degrees of freedom. If suspended vertically, it will oscillate like a pendulum, and vibrate axially too, etc.

4

spring of length l.† The work done in causing a displacement x is represented by the shaded area in Fig. 2.1B, which gives the strain or potential energy V stored in the spring. Thus

$$V = \int_0^x f\,dx = sx^2/2. \qquad 2.1$$

3. THE DIFFERENTIAL EQUATION By obtaining and then solving this, we can discuss the motion of the system. Since there is no driving or external force acting, the condition to be satisfied is that the sum of the internal forces must vanish. At any displacement $x \neq 0$, there are two forces, (a) sx the spring force tending to restore m to its central position 0, (b) the

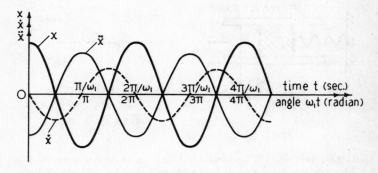

Fig. 3.1

inertial force md^2x/dt^2 by virtue of acceleration or deceleration, according as m is moving towards or away from 0. Thus

$$m\ddot{x} + sx = 0, \qquad 3.1$$

or $$\ddot{x} + \omega_1^2 x = 0, \qquad 3.2$$

where $\omega_1 = (s/m)^{1/2}$. The complete solution of 3.2, with two arbitrary constants, is

---

†In general, stiffness = df/dx, which varies with x if the characteristic is non-linear. For *unit* length of spring, the stiffness in the linear case is sl.

$$x = A \cos \omega_1 t + B \sin \omega_1 t \qquad 3.3$$

$$= C \cos (\omega_1 t - \epsilon), \qquad 3.4$$

where $C = (A^2 + B^2)^{1/2}$, $\epsilon = \tan^{-1}(B/A)$.

To determine A, B, we have to specify 'initial' conditions, i.e. the displacement and velocity of m at $t = 0$.* Suppose the spring is extended by x_0 and released at $t = 0$. The initial conditions are $x = x_0$, $\dot{x} = 0$. Substituting the first into 3.3 gives $A = x_0$. Differentiating 3.3

$$\dot{x} = \omega_1(-A \sin \omega_1 t + B \cos \omega_1 t), \qquad 3.5$$

and for the condition $\dot{x} = 0$, $B = 0$. Inserting A, B, into 3.3 yields

$$x = x_0 \cos \omega_1 t, \qquad 3.6$$

which gives the displacement of m from 0 at any time $t \geq 0$. The angular frequency of the motion is ω_1, the frequency in cycles per second $\omega_1/2\pi$, and the periodic time $2\pi/\omega_1$. By virtue of the cosinusoidal relationship, the motion of m is said to be *harmonic*. It is evident from 3.4 that whatever A, B, and, therefore, the initial conditions, the motion of m will be harmonic, since ϵ affects merely its phase.

By 3.6 the velocity of m is

$$\dot{x} = -\omega_1 x_0 \sin \omega_1 t = \omega_1 x \cos (\omega_1 t + \pi/2), \qquad 3.7$$

and the acceleration

$$\ddot{x} = -\omega_1^2 x_0 \cos \omega_1 t = \omega_1^2 x_0 \cos (\omega_1 t + \pi). \qquad 3.8$$

By 3.6, 3.7, the phase of the velocity is $\pi/2$ in advance of the displacement, while by 3.6, 3.8, the acceleration is opposite to the displacement, i.e. π radians† in advance. The phase relationships are shown by the graphs in Fig. 3.1.

---

*The number of arbitrary constants and initial conditions is the same as the order of the differential equation.

†This is π/ω_1 seconds, since $(\omega_1 t + \pi) = \omega_1(t + \pi/\omega_1)$.

4. ENERGY EQUATION Writing $dx/dt = v$, we get $d^2x/dt^2 = (dv/dx)(dx/dt) = v\,dv/dx$. Substituting into 3.1 gives

$$mv\,dv/dx + sx = 0. \qquad 4.1$$

Multiplying throughout by dx and integrating, we obtain

$$m \int v\,dv + s \int x\,dx = C, \qquad \text{a constant,} \qquad 4.2$$

and the energy equation is

$$mv^2/2 + sx^2/2 = C. \qquad 4.3$$

This asserts that the sum of the kinetic energy of m, and the potential energy of s, is constant for all $|x| \leq x_0$, and $t \geq 0$. When $x = x_0$, $v = 0$, so

$$C = sx_0^2/2, \qquad 4.4$$

and when $x = 0$, $v = v_{max}$, so

$$C = mv_{max}^2/2, \qquad 4.5$$

these corresponding to the extreme and central positions, respectively.

Hence $\qquad\qquad sx_0^2/2 = mv_{max}^2/2, \qquad\qquad 4.6$

and the maximum potential (strain) and kinetic energies are equal. By 4.3, 4.4, the energy equation may be written

$$mv^2/2 = (x_0 - x^2)/2. \qquad 4.7$$

5. ELECTRICAL ANALOG Referring to Fig. 5.1, suppose the capacitance has a charge Q, and at $t = 0$ the switch is closed.

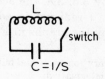

Fig. 5.1

Electrical oscillations will ensue. If I is the instantaneous current, since the sum of the p.d.s in the circuit must vanish, the D.E. is

$$L \, dI/dt + S \int I \, dt = 0, \qquad 5.1$$

where the elastance $S = I/C$. Now $I = \dot{Q}$, so

$$L\ddot{Q} + SQ = 0. \qquad 5.2$$

This is identical in form with 3.1, and the mechanical and electrical systems are analogous, provided $x \sim Q$, $m \sim L$, $s \sim S = I/C$. Further, since $I = Q$, it follows that $\dot{x} \sim I$. Thus displacement is analogous to quantity of electricity, mass to inductance, stiffness to elastance (or compliance to capacitance), and velocity to current.

Hence by 3.6, 3.7, 4.3, 4.4,

$$Q = Q_0 \cos \omega_1 t, \qquad I = -\omega_1 Q_0 \sin \omega_1 t, \qquad 5.3$$

$$\omega_1 = (S/L)^{1/2} = I/(LC)^{1/2}, \text{ and } LI^2/2 + SQ^2/2 = SQ_0^2/2. \quad 5.4$$

Thus the sum of the electromagnetic and electrostatic energies in the system is constant, being independent of time. When $Q = 0$ the energy is wholly electromagnetic, and when $I = 0$, wholly electrostatic.

6. MASS SUSPENDED FROM SPRING This is illustrated in Fig. 6.1A. The weight or gravitational force $W = mg$ causes an extension $h = mg/s$, which fixes the equilibrium position, i.e. it in effect moves the origin from $x = 0$ to $x = h$. Accordingly in 3.2 we write $(x - h)$ for h, and obtain

$$\ddot{x} + \omega_1^2 x = \omega_1^2 h, \qquad 6.1$$

of which the complete solution with two arbitrary constants is

$$x = A \cos \omega_1 t + B \sin \omega_1 t + h, \qquad 6.2$$

or $\qquad (x - h) = A \cos \omega_1 t + B \sin \omega_1 t. \qquad 6.3$

Hence motion of the mass in the systems of Figs. 2.1A, 6.1A about their respective equilibrium positions, is identical.

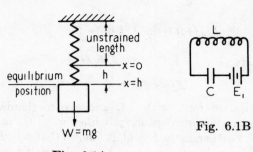

Fig. 6.1B

Fig. 6.1A

★*Electrical analog.* This is shown in Fig. 6.1B, where E_1 is a constant p.d. analogous to the force *mg*. The D.E. is

$$L \, dI/dt + S \int I \, dt = E_1 = SQ_1 , \qquad 6.4$$

where Q_1 is the charge on C corresponding to a p.d. E_1. Then with $I = \dot{Q}$, 6.4 becomes

$$L\ddot{Q} + S(Q - Q_1) = 0, \qquad 6.5$$

or

$$\ddot{Q} + \omega_1^2 Q = \omega_1^2 Q_1 . \qquad 6.6$$

Comparison with 6.1 shows that $h \sim Q_1$. The complete solution of 6.6 is, by 6.2

$$Q = A \, \cos \omega_1 t + B \sin \omega_1 t + Q_1 ; \qquad 6.7$$

also

$$I = \dot{Q} = \omega_1(-A \sin \omega_1 t + B \cos \omega_1 t). \qquad 6.8$$

If $Q = Q_0$, and $I = 0$ when $t = 0$, 6.7 gives $A = (Q_0 - Q_1)$, while from 6.8 $B = 0$. Using these values in 6.7, 6.8, yields

$$Q = (Q_0 - Q_1) \, \cos \omega_1 t, \qquad 6.9$$

and

$$I = -\omega_1(Q_0 - Q_1) \sin \omega_1 t. \qquad 6.10$$

7. PNEUMATIC STIFFNESS   Fig. 7.1 depicts a sealed enclosure of volume v_0 fitted with a short tube in which a *rigid* disk of area A and mass m_d can move freely. If displaced either inwards

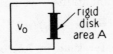

Fig. 7.1

or outwards, the disk will oscillate along its axis, in virtue of the 'stiffness' due to the enclosed air. Assuming adiabatic change, we have

$$pv^\gamma = C, \qquad \text{a constant,} \qquad 7.1$$

so
$$d(pv^\gamma)/dx = \gamma pv^{\gamma-1} dv/dx + v^\gamma dp/dx = 0. \qquad 7.2$$

Multiplying by $Av^{-\gamma}$ gives

$$(\gamma pA/v)(dv/dx) = -A(dp/dx) = s, \qquad 7.3$$

the stiffness or force per unit displacement. The minus sign indicates that p increases with decrease in v, and vice-versa, in virtue of the negative slope of the adiabatic curve. Since $dv = A dx$, if p_0 is the static external air pressure, 7.3 gives

$$s = \gamma A p_0/v_0 . \qquad 7.4$$

This is valid provided, (a) the displacement is such that the working arc of the 'characteristic' may be represented adequately by its tangent, (b) the internal pressure change is almost in phase everywhere, i.e. the wave length of sound $\gg$ the largest dimension of the enclosure.

During vibration, the mass of the disk is increased by virtue of the cyclically varying motion of the air in its neighborhood.* The additional mass is termed the 'accession to inertia' m_i [10]. For a disk radius a metre, as in Fig. 7.1, it is sensibly constant if $a\omega < 140$, but decreases with increase in ω thereafter. The

---

*Outside the enclosure.

total mass is $m_d + m_i = m$, so by §3, the natural frequency

$$\omega_1 = (s/m)^{1/2} = \{\gamma A p_0/v_0(m_d + m_i)\}^{1/2}. \qquad 7.5$$

If the disk were suspended by a narrow annular surround of axial stiffness s_1, the total stiffness would be $s + s_1$, so

$$\omega_1 = \{(s + s_1)/m\}^{1/2}, \qquad 7.6$$

where m would be greater than in 7.5, owing to the mass of part of the annulus, and additional accession to inertia.

8. REDUCED DISCRETE SYSTEM   Systems of the type indicated in Fig. 8.1A, C having more than one spring, may be reduced

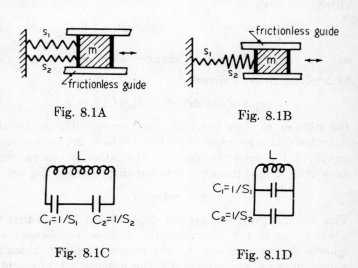

Fig. 8.1A

Fig. 8.1B

Fig. 8.1C

Fig. 8.1D

to an equivalent single mass-spring arrangement. In the language of electrical technology, the springs in Fig. 8.1A are in series, while those in Fig. 8.1C are in parallel. The combined stiffness in the first case is $s = (s_1 + s_2)$, which is analogous to elastances S_1, S_2, (Fig. 8.1B) in series. For the second case, neglecting the weight of the springs if m were suspended from them, a force f causes extensions $x_1 = f/s_1$, and $x_2 = f/s_2$, respectively. Thus the total extension is

$$x = x_1 + x_2 = f/s_1 + f/s_2 = f(1/s_1 + 1/s_2), \qquad 8.1$$

so the stiffness of the combination is

$$s = \text{force/extension} = 1/(1/s_1 + 1/s_2) = s_1 s_2/(s_1 + s_2), \qquad 8.2$$

and $s <$ either s_1 or s_2. This is analogous to the elastances S_1, S_2, (Fig. 8.1D) in parallel. The reduced system in either case, being described completely by one coordinate, has one degree of freedom, and the angular frequency is $\omega_1 = (s/m)^{1/2}$.

9. LATERAL VIBRATION OF LOADED UNIFORM BAR   Referring to Fig. 9.1, we suppose the bar is vertical in its equilibrium

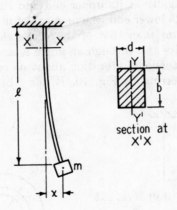

Fig. 9.1

position, and that its mass is negligible in comparison with that of m. The relationship between static horizontal force f and small displacement x is, neglecting the influence of the weight of the bar and that of m,

$$x = fl^3/3EI, \qquad 9.1$$

where I is the moment of inertia of the *section* of the bar about $Y'Y$, and E the modulus of elasticity. Since l^3/EI is constant,

9.1 is a linear relationship of the form $f = sx$ as in §2, so the *equivalent* stiffness of the bar is

$$s = 3EI/l^3. \qquad 9.2$$

For a bar of rectangular section, $I = bd^3/12$, so

$$s = Ebd^3/4l^3, \qquad 9.3$$

and, therefore, the frequency of the lateral vibration is

$$\omega_1 = (s/m)^{1/2} = (Ebd^3/ml^3)^{1/2}/2. \qquad 9.4$$

The electrical analog is that in Fig. 5.1.

10. TORSIONAL VIBRATION   A uniform shaft or bar of circular section is fixed rigidly at its upper end and supports a homogeneous disk at its lower end, the moment of inertia of the disk being much greater than that of the whole shaft. If the disk is rotated about its axis through an angle θ_0 and then released, it will execute a torsional vibration about its equilibrium position $\theta = 0$. Referring to Fig. 10.1B, let f be the tangential

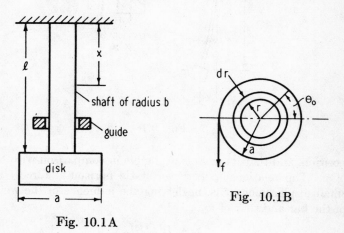

Fig. 10.1A

Fig. 10.1B

force at the periphery of the disk of radius a, then the applied torque or twisting moment is fa. If the torque to cause a rotation

θ at the disk is τ, for a limited range of θ we have the linear relationship

$$\tau = \gamma\theta, \qquad\qquad 10.1$$

where γ is the torque-stiffness or torque to cause an angular movement of 1 radian, if the shaft remained elastic. γ^{-1} is the torque-compliance. For a uniform shaft radius b, free length l,

$$\gamma = \pi b^4 G/2l = GI/l, \qquad\qquad 10.2$$

G being the modulus of rigidity, and I the polar moment of inertia of the *section*.

The condition to be satisfied during vibration (after removal of f) is that the sum of the internal torques shall be zero. The torque due to the resisting moment of the shaft is given by 10.1, and neglecting the inertia of the shaft, there remains the inertial torque due to the disk, which we now calculate. Referring to Fig. 10.1B, the mass of an elemental ring of radius r is $2\pi\rho h r\,dr$, ρ being the density of the material. The peripheral velocity of the ring is $d(r\theta)/dt = r\,d\theta/dt$, and its moment of momentum

$$(2\pi\rho h r\,dr)r^2\dot\theta = (2\pi\rho h r^3\,dr)\dot\theta. \qquad\qquad 10.3$$

The time rate of change of the moment of momentum of the ring is equal to the inertial torque, so

$$d\tau_1 = (2\pi\rho h r^3\,dr)\ddot\theta. \qquad\qquad 10.4$$

For the whole disk

$$\tau_1 = 2\pi\rho h\ddot\theta\int_0^a r^3\,dr = (\rho\pi a^4 h/2)\ddot\theta, \qquad\qquad 10.5$$

$$= I\ddot\theta, \qquad\qquad 10.6$$

where $I = \rho\pi a^4 h/2 = ma^2/2$, is the polar m.o.i. of the disk.

Then by 10.1, 10.6, the above condition is satisfied if

$$I\ddot\theta + \gamma\theta = 0, \qquad\qquad 10.7$$

or $$\ddot\theta + \omega_1^2\theta = 0, \qquad\qquad 10.8$$

where $\omega_1^2 = \gamma/\mathbf{I}$. This D.E. is identical in form with 3.2, so its complete solution is

$$\theta = A \cos \omega_1 t + B \sin \omega_1 t, \qquad 10.9$$

and the angular frequency about the axis is $\omega_1 = (2\gamma/\rho\pi a^4 h)^{1/2} = (b/a)^2 (G/\rho h)^{1/2}/l^{1/2}$. In this case $\mathbf{I} \sim L$, $\gamma \sim S$, $\theta \sim Q$, $\dot{\theta} \sim I$, and the electrical analog is the circuit in Fig. 5.1.

11. STEPPED SHAFT   When the shaft has two parts of radii b_1, b_2, lengths l_1, l_2, and respective torque-stiffnesses γ_1, γ_2, the combined stiffness is less than that of either shaft alone, since the angles of twist on the lengths l_1, l_2, are additive. The arrangement is analogous to two springs in parallel as in Fig. 8.1C, so by 8.2 the combined torque-stiffness is

$$\gamma = \gamma_1 \gamma_2/(\gamma_1 + \gamma_2), \qquad 11.1$$

and the angular frequency of vibration with a disk at the free end is

$$\omega_1 = \{\gamma_1 \gamma_2/(\gamma_1 + \gamma_2)\mathbf{I}\}^{1/2} \qquad 11.2$$

Now $\gamma_1 = \pi b_1^4 G/2l_1$, $\gamma_2 = \pi b_2^4 G/2l_2$, $\mathbf{I} = \rho\pi a^4 h/2$,

so $$\gamma = \pi(b_1 b_2)^4 G/2(b_1^4 l_2 + b_2^4 l_1), \qquad 11.3$$

and, therefore, by 11.1—11.3

$$\omega_1 = (b_1/a)^2 (G/\rho h)^{1/2}/\{l_1 + (b_1/b_2)^4 l_2\}^{1/2}. \qquad 11.4$$

Comparing this with the formula in §10, it is evident that $l = \{l_1 + (b_1/b_2)^4 l_2\}$ is the length of the equivalent shaft of radius b_1 and stiffness γ (from 11.1).

★12. INFLUENCE OF MASS OF COIL SPRING IN §3   A suitably mounted spring can vibrate axially,* by virtue of its distributed mass and stiffness. If one end is anchored and the other statically

---

*It can of course vibrate laterally and torsionally, but we are now considering axial motion only.

displaced by ξ_0 , the displacement of any intermediate point distant x from the anchorage is $\xi = \xi_0 x/l$, l being the unstrained length. When released, axial oscillation ensues, and in absence of loss, an infinity of modes is present (§71). Loss being unavoidable in practice, the modes of higher frequency are quenched quickly, the fundamental predominates, and then $\xi_{max} \simeq \xi_0 \sin(\pi x/2l)$. With m attached ($m_s \ll m$), the frequency is much less than the fundamental of the spring alone, and the relationship between ξ_{max} and x is almost $\xi_{max} = \xi_0 x/l$, the static value. This means that the dynamic deformation curve of the spring is determined mainly by its stiffness, the influence of its mass being small. By *assuming* the above linear relationship, a constraint is introduced, in effect, and the potential energy of the spring is just in excess of the actual value. Consequently the calculated frequency is slightly higher than the observed value, although in most applications the difference between the two is negligible. Similar considerations are involved where the influence of the mass of a bar in lateral motion, or a shaft executing torsional oscillations is concerned.

Referring to Fig. 12.1, if **m** is the mass per unit length of spring, the max. kinetic energy of an element dx is $(\mathbf{m}\,dx)v_{max}^2/2$.

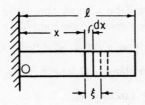

Fig. 12.1

The motion at any point x is $\xi = \xi_{max} \cos \omega_1 t = \xi_0(x/l) \cos \omega_1 t$, so $|v_{max}| = \omega_1 \xi_0(x/l)$, and

$$dT = (\mathbf{m}\omega_1^2\xi_0^2/2l^2)x^2\,dx, \qquad\qquad 12.1$$

ω_1 being the frequency of the *loaded* spring. Hence the max. K.E. of the whole spring is

$$T = (m\omega_1^2\xi_0^2/2l^2) \int_0^l x^2 \, dx \qquad 12.2$$

$$= (ml/3)(\omega_1^2\xi_0^2/2). \qquad 12.3$$

This represents the K.E. of a mass one third that of the spring, fixed to its free end. Accordingly if $m_s \ll m$, the system of Fig. 2.1A is equivalent to a massless spring of stiffness s loaded by a mass $(m + m_s/3)$ at its free end. The lowest angular frequency of the combination is

$$\omega_1 = \{s/(m + m_s/3)\}^{1/2} = (s/m)^{1/2}/(1 + m_s/3m)^{1/2} \qquad 12.4$$

$$\simeq (s/m)^{1/2}(1 - m_s/6m), \qquad 12.5$$

so the influence of the spring mass is to reduce ω_1 by approximately $16.7m_s/m$ per cent. The percentage error in 12.4 is 0.5, 0.75, 3 according as $m_s/m = 0.5, 1, 2$, respectively.

★13. INFLUENCE OF MASS OF BAR IN §9 Assuming that m_b, the mass of the bar, is small compared with m, the dynamic deformation curve will be almost the same as the static one. Then for small displacements (see Fig. 75.1)

$$\xi = \xi_0(3l - x)x^2/2l^3. \qquad 13.1$$

The max. K.E. of an elemental length dx is

$$dT = (m \, dx)\omega_1^2\xi_{max}^2/2 \qquad 13.2$$

$$= \{m\omega_1^2\xi_0^2(3l - x)^2x^4/8l^6\} \, dx. \qquad 13.3$$

Thus for the whole bar

$$T = (m\omega_1^2\xi_0^2/8l^6) \int_0^l (9l^2 - 6lx + x^2)x^4 \, dx \qquad 13.4$$

$$= (33\,ml/140)\omega_1^2\xi_0^2/2. \qquad 13.5$$

This represents the K.E. of a mass 33/140 that of the bar fixed at its free end. Hence if $m_b \ll m$, the system of Fig. 9.1 is equivalent to a massless bar of stiffness s given at 9.2, loaded at its free end by a mass $(m + 33m_b/140)$. If $m = 0$, the error in the frequency of the lowest mode is only 1.5 per cent. It is left to the reader to show that

$$\omega_1 \simeq (s/m)^{1/2}(1 - 33m_b/280m). \qquad 13.6$$

★14. INFLUENCE OF SHAFT INERTIA IN §10 Referring to Fig. 10.1, the mass of an elemental ring of radius r, thickness dr and depth h, is $\rho 2\pi h r \, dr$. If $\dot\theta$ is angular velocity, the peripheral velocity of the ring is $\dot\theta r$, and its K.E.

$$dT = \rho\pi\dot\theta^2 h r^3 \, dr. \qquad 14.1$$

For the whole disk

$$T = \rho\pi\dot\theta^2 h \int_0^a r^3 \, dr = [\rho\pi a^4 h/2](\dot\theta^2/2) \qquad 14.2$$

$$= I\dot\theta^2/2, \qquad 14.3$$

this being the K.E. at any instant when the angular velocity of the disk is $\dot\theta$ radians per second.

The moment of inertia of an elemental length of shaft dx, is $\rho\pi b^4 \, dx/2$. If the m.o.i. of the whole shaft is much less than that of the disk, the dynamic relationship between angular twist and x will be almost that obtained statically, since the influence of the shaft is due mainly to torque-stiffness. Thus the angular velocity at x is $\dot\theta x/l$, and the K.E. of the element is $dI_s(\dot\theta x/l)^2/2$, so

$$dT = \rho\pi b^4 \dot\theta^2 x^2 \, dx/4l^2. \qquad 14.4$$

For the whole shaft

$$T = (\rho\pi b^4 \dot\theta^2/4l^2) \int_0^l x^2 \, dx = (\rho\pi b^4 l/6)(\dot\theta^2/2) \qquad 14.5$$

$$= (I_s/3)(\dot\theta^2/2), \qquad 14.6$$

where I_s is the m.o.i. of the shaft. 14.6 represents the K.E. of a disk at $x = l$, whose m.o.i. is $1/3$ that of the shaft. Hence if $I_s \ll I$, the system of Fig. 10.1A is equivalent to a massless shaft of torque-stiffness γ, having a mass with m.o.i. $(I + I_s/3)$ at its free end. From §10 it may be deduced that the angular frequency of the torsional vibration is

$$\omega_1 \simeq (\gamma/I)^{1/2}(1 - I_s/6I). \qquad 14.7$$

15. DAMPING LOSS   In §4 we showed that the *total* energy of a loss-free system having one degree of freedom, is independent of both time and displacement. But in practice there must be loss, so we shall study its influence on the vibrational characteristics of the system. In the electrical case, the p.d. across a resistance R is $E = RI$, and by §5 the mechanical analog is force $= r\dot{x}$, where r is the resisting force per unit velocity. r may vary with $\dot{x}$, so in order to effect simplification, we compromise and consider r to be an 'idealised' mechanical resistance whose electrical analog is R. A mechanical resistance of this type causes viscous damping akin to that obtained with a fluid dash-pot.

16. THE DIFFERENTIAL EQUATION   For free oscillation the sum of the internal forces must vanish, so (Fig. 16.1)

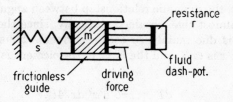

Fig. 16.1

$$(\text{inertive} + \text{resistive} + \text{elastive}) \text{ force} = 0, \qquad 16.1$$

or
$$m\ddot{x} + r\dot{x} + sx = 0. \qquad 16.2$$

It is convenient to write this in the form

$$\ddot{x} + 2\kappa\dot{x} + \omega_1^2 x = 0, \qquad 16.3$$

where $\kappa = r/2m$, and $\omega_1 = (s/m)^{1/2}$, the angular frequency of the system *undamped*. To solve 16.3 we shall put it in the simple form 3.2 by writing $x = e^{-\kappa t}u$, u being a twice differentiable function of t. Substituting into 16.3 yields

$$\ddot{u} + \alpha^2 u = 0, \qquad 16.4$$

with $\alpha^2 = (\omega_1^2 - \kappa^2)$. Then by 3.2

$$u = A \cos \alpha t + B \sin \alpha t, \qquad 16.5$$

so $\qquad x = e^{-\kappa t}u = e^{-\kappa t}(A \cos \alpha t + B \sin \alpha t), \qquad 16.6$

$$= e^{-\kappa t}C \cos (\alpha t - \epsilon), \qquad 16.7$$

where $C = (A^2 + B^2)^{1/2}$, $\epsilon = \tan^{-1}(B/A)$ are arbitrary constants.

Since α may be real, imaginary or zero, there are three cases to be considered, (i) $\omega_1 > \kappa$, (ii) $\omega_1 < \kappa$, (iii) $\omega_1 = \kappa$. For (i) the solution is 16.7, which represents a harmonic motion exponentially damped, and $x \to 0$ as $t \to +\infty$. The angular frequency of the *harmonic* component is $\alpha = (\omega_1^2 - \kappa^2)^{1/2}$, whereas in the undamped system $\kappa = 0$ and $\alpha = \omega_1$. Hence the influence of damping is twofold: (a) the amplitude of the vibration decays exponentially with increase in time, (b) the angular frequency of the harmonic component is reduced* from ω_1 to $(\omega_1^2 - \kappa^2)^{1/2}$.

(ii). Here $\alpha^2 = -(\kappa^2 - \omega_1^2)$, so $\alpha = \pm i\beta$, with $\beta = (\kappa^2 - \omega_1^2)^{1/2} = \kappa\{1 - (\omega_1/\kappa)^2\}^{1/2}$, being real > 0. Choosing $+ i\beta$ conventionally, and substituting into 16.6 yields

$$x = e^{-\kappa t}(A \cosh \beta t + B \sinh \beta t), \qquad 16.8$$

where B, being an *arbitrary* constant, replaces iB. 16.8 shows that the motion is not oscillatory as in (i); for $\genfrac{}{}{0pt}{}{\cosh}{\sinh}\}\beta t =$

---

*In virtue of resistance, the *net* restoring force of the spring acting on m is reduced. With $\kappa = 0$, $s = m\omega_1^2$, but for $\kappa > 0$, the equivalent stiffness is $m(\omega_1^2 - \kappa^2)$, i.e. a reduction of $m\kappa^2$.

$(e^{\beta t} \pm e^{-\beta t})/2$, and since $\beta = \kappa\{1 - (\omega_1/\kappa)^2\}^{1/2} < \kappa$, it follows that $x \to 0$ as $t \to +\infty$, without oscillation. The form of decay curve depends upon the initial conditions and is discussed later.

(iii). Here $\alpha = 0$, and 16.5 is *not* the solution of the D.E. From 16.4 with $\alpha = 0$,

$$\ddot{u} = 0, \quad \text{so} \quad \dot{u} = A, \quad \text{a constant,} \qquad 16.9$$

and, therefore, $\qquad u = At + B, \qquad\qquad\qquad 16.10$

which gives $\qquad x = e^{-\kappa t}(At + B). \qquad\qquad 16.11$

This is known as the 'critical' case, being the dividing line between (i), (ii), where κ is such that the oscillation is just extinguished, and $x \to 0$ as $t \to +\infty$.

17. INITIAL CONDITIONS

For generality we have $x = x_0$, $\dot{x} = x_1$, at $t = 0$, and from these the arbitrary constants* may be found.

(i). If m is displaced by x_0 and released at $t = 0$, then $x_1 = 0$. Inserting the first condition into 16.6 gives $A = x_0$. Differentiating 16.6 yields

$$\dot{x} = e^{-\kappa t}\{\alpha(-A \sin \alpha t + B \cos \alpha t)$$
$$\qquad\qquad 17.1$$
$$- \kappa(A \cos \alpha t + B \sin \alpha t)\}.$$

Using the second condition leads to

$$\alpha B - \kappa A = 0, \quad \text{so} \quad B = \kappa x_0/\alpha. \qquad 17.2$$

Substituting for A, B, into 16.6, we obtain

$$x = x_0 e^{-\kappa t}\{\cos \alpha t + (\kappa/\alpha) \sin \alpha t\} \qquad 17.3$$

$$= x_0\{1 + (\kappa/\alpha)^2\}^{1/2} e^{-\kappa t} \cos \{\alpha t - \tan^{-1} (\kappa/\alpha)\}. \qquad 17.4$$

---

*An *arbitrary* constant may be real, imaginary or complex, but it must be independent of the variables x, t. When initial conditions are assigned, A, B, depend upon them and cease to be arbitrary. Originally they are arbitrary in a mathematical sense.

This expression is portrayed graphically in Fig. 17.1A, being a damped cosine curve with envelopes $\pm x_0\{1 + (\kappa/\alpha)^2\}^{1/2}e^{-\kappa t}$.

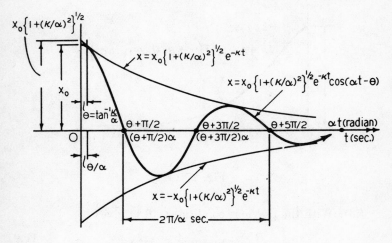

Fig. 17.1A

The zeros occur when

$$\cos\{\alpha t - \tan^{-1}(\kappa/\alpha)\} = 0,$$

so
$$t = (1/\alpha)\{(2n - 1)\pi/2 + \tan^{-1}(\kappa/\alpha)\}, \qquad 17.5$$

$n = 1, 2, \cdots$. If $\kappa = 0$, $\alpha = \omega_1$, and 17.4 reduces to 3.6.

(ii). Applying the initial conditions in (i) to 16.8 gives $A = x_0$, and

$$[e^{-\kappa t}\{\beta(A\sinh\beta t + B\cosh\beta t)$$
$$\qquad\qquad\qquad\qquad 17.6$$
$$- \kappa(A\cosh\beta t + B\sinh\beta t)\}]_{t=0} = 0.$$

Thus
$$B = \kappa x_0/\beta, \qquad 17.7$$

and 16.8 becomes

$$x = x_0 e^{-\kappa t}\{\cosh\beta t + (\kappa/\beta)\sinh\beta t\}. \qquad 17.8$$

17.8 represents the monotonically (without oscillation) decreasing function depicted in 17.1B.

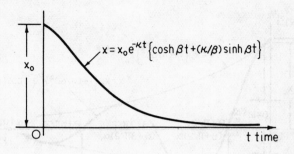

$$x = x_0 e^{-\kappa t}\{\cosh \beta t + (\kappa/\beta)\sinh \beta t\}$$

Fig. 17.1B

(iii). With the previous conditions, 16.11 gives

$$B = x_0 , \qquad A = \kappa x_0 , \qquad\qquad 17.9$$

so

$$x = x_0 e^{-\kappa t}(\kappa t + 1). \qquad\qquad 17.10$$

This has a maximum at $t = 0$, and an inflexion at $t = \kappa^{-1}$, as shown in Fig. 17.1C.

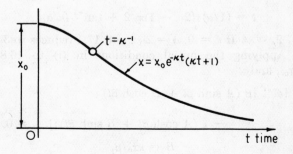

$$t = \kappa^{-1}$$

$$x = x_0 e^{-\kappa t}(\kappa t + 1)$$

Fig. 17.1C

★18. ELECTRICAL ANALOG OF SYSTEM IN §16   This is shown
in Fig. 18.1, the D.E. being

$$L \, dI/dt + RI + S \int I dt = 0, \qquad 18.1$$

or $$L\ddot{Q} + R\dot{Q} + SQ = 0, \qquad 18.2$$

which is identical in form with 16.2. Hence by substituting the
analogs in the formulae of §§16, 17, those for the electrical circuit may be obtained immediately.

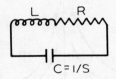

Fig. 18.1

Fig. 18.1 is also the analog for damped torsional oscillations,
e.g. if we imagine the disk in Fig. 10.1A to be immersed in oil.
The D.E. is

$$I\ddot{\theta} + \sigma\dot{\theta} + \gamma\theta = 0, \qquad 18.3$$

where $\sigma \sim R$ is the torque-resistance (moment of resistance)
per unit angular velocity, due to viscous damping.

CHAPTER II

Forced Vibrations of Simple Linear Systems: Impulses

19. LOSS-FREE SYSTEM   We consider m in Fig. 2.1A to be driven along the axis of the spring by an alternating force

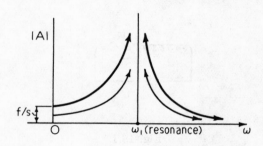

Fig. 19.1A

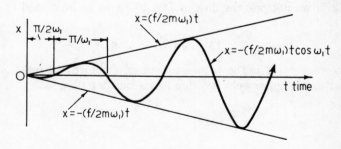

Fig. 19.1B

$f \sin \omega t$. The sum of the internal must be equal to the external force, i.e. the algebraic sum of the forces must vanish, so

$$(m\ddot{x} + sx) - f \sin \omega t = 0. \qquad 19.1$$

With $\omega_1^2 = s/m$, $f_1 = f/m$, 19.1 becomes

$$\ddot{x} + \omega_1^2 x = f_1 \sin \omega t. \qquad 19.2$$

The solution has two parts, namely, the complementary function, and the particular integral. The c.f. is the solution at 3.3

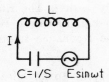

Fig. 19.2

when the r.h.s. is zero, and it gives the natural oscillations of the system, which commence on application of the driving force. To derive the p.i. when $\omega \neq \omega_1$, assume that

$$x = A \sin \omega t + B \cos \omega t. \qquad 19.3$$

Substituting into 19.2 we get

$$-\omega^2(A \sin \omega t + B \cos \omega t) + \omega_1^2(A \sin \omega t + B \cos \omega t)$$

$$= f_1 \sin \omega t. \qquad 19.4$$

Equating the coefficients of $\sin \omega t$, $\cos \omega t$, on both sides of 19.4, yields

$$A = f_1/(\omega_1^2 - \omega^2), \qquad B = 0. \qquad 19.5$$

Then by 19.3, 19.5 the displacement corresponding to the forced oscillation of frequency ω, is

$$x = \{f/m(\omega_1^2 - \omega^2)\} \sin \omega t. \qquad 19.6$$

The amplitude is

$$|A| = (f/m\omega_1^2)/|1 - a^2|, \qquad 19.7$$

where $a = \omega/\omega_1$. When $\omega \to 0$, $|A| \to f/m\omega_1^2 = f/s$, the static displacement. As $\omega \to \omega_1$, from either the upper or the lower side, $|A| \rightarrow +\infty$. When $\omega = \omega_1$, 19.6 is *not* the p.i. of 19.2. It is then

$$x = -(f/2m\omega_1)t \cos \omega_1 t, \qquad 19.8$$

so $$|A| = (f/2m\omega_1)t, \qquad 19.9$$

which increases linearly with t. The r.h.s. of 19.7, 19.8, are depicted graphically in Fig. 19.1A, B. Beyond the point $\omega = \omega_1$, usually called the resonance frequency, $|A|$ decreases monotonically.

Limitation of ω. 19.1 applies to an 'idealised' discrete system where m and s are 'pure' mass and stiffness, respectively (see §1). The D.E. is valid in practice provided (a) $m_s \ll m$, (b) the fundamental frequency of the spring, if considered to be fixed at both ends, is much greater than the driving frequency ω. By §72, the spring frequency is $\pi c/l = \pi(s/m_s)^{1/2}$, c being the velocity of wave motion. Accordingly we must have $\omega \ll \pi(s/m_s)^{1/2}$. Since $s = m\omega_1^2$, this inequality may be written $(m/m_s) \gg (\omega/\pi\omega_1)^2$.

Electrical analog. This is shown in Fig. 19.2, where potential difference (or e.m.f.) is analogous to mechanical force, i.e. $f \sim E$.

★20. PHASE RELATIONSHIPS By 19.2 and 19.6, the displacement of m is in phase with the driving force, provided $\omega < \omega_1$. When $\omega > \omega_1$, the two are in anti-phase, so in passing through the resonance point, the phase alters by π radians. From 19.6

$$\dot{x} = \{\omega f/m(\omega_1^2 - \omega^2)\} \cos \omega t, \qquad 20.1$$

and since $\pm \cos \omega t = \sin (\omega t \pm \pi/2)$, there is a phase difference of $\pm\pi/2$ between the velocity of m and the driving force, according as $\omega < \omega_1$, or $\omega > \omega_1$. The acceleration of m is

$$\ddot{x} = -\{\omega^2 f/m(\omega_1^2 - \omega^2)\} \sin \omega t, \qquad 20.2$$

$$= -\omega^2 x, \qquad 20.3$$

so that driving force and acceleration are in phase or in antiphase according as ω is above or below resonance.

21. MECHANICAL IMPEDANCE   In 19.1 take $fe^{i\omega t}$ instead of $f \sin \omega t$, then with $x = \int^t v \, dt$, $\dot{x} = v$, we get

$$m\dot{v} + s \int^t v \, dt = fe^{i\omega t}. \qquad 21.1$$

For the forced vibration let $v = v_1 e^{i\omega t}$, and 21.1 gives

$$i\omega m v_1 + s v_1/i\omega = f, \qquad 21.2$$

so
$$v_1(i\omega m - is/\omega) = f. \qquad 21.3$$

The mechanical input or *driving point* impedance is defined to be

$$z = \text{force/velocity} = i(\omega m - s/\omega), \qquad 21.4$$

this being analogous to the electrical case. Thus $i\omega m$ is the mass reactance of m, and $-is/\omega$ the stiffness reactance of s. Since $s = \omega_1^2 m$, 21.4 may be written

$$z = i\omega m\{ 1 - (\omega_1/\omega)^2\}. \qquad 21.5$$

Thus when $s/\omega > \omega m$, $\omega < \omega_1$ (below resonance), and the impedance is due mainly to stiffness reactance, whereas when $\omega m > s/\omega$, $\omega > \omega_1$ (above resonance), and z is due mainly to mass reactance. At resonance $\omega = \omega_1$ and z vanishes.

Torsional vibration.   Replacing f in Fig. 10.1B by $fe^{i\omega t}$, the D.E. analogous to 21.1 is (see 10.7),

$$I\dot{\zeta} + \gamma \int^t \zeta \, dt = fae^{i\omega t}, \qquad 21.6$$

where ζ is the angular velocity at the disk. Writing $\zeta = \zeta_1 e^{i\omega t}$ leads to

$$i\zeta_1(\omega I - \gamma/\omega) = fa, \qquad 21.7$$

so the mechanical impedance at radius a is

$$\text{force/linear vel.} = f/a\zeta_1 = i(\omega\mathbf{I} - \gamma/\omega)/a^2. \qquad 21.8$$

★22. EFFECTIVE MASS   It is sometimes convenient to consider the reactive part of a mechanical impedance as an effective mass [10], which varies with ω. 21.4 may be written

$$z = i\omega(m - s/\omega^2) = i\omega m_e , \qquad 22.1$$

where $m_e = (m - s/\omega^2)$ is defined to be the effective mass as presented *at the driving point* on m. The graphical relationship

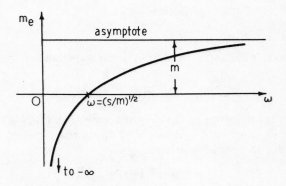

Fig. 22.1

between m_e and ω is indicated in Fig. 22.1. As $\omega \to 0$, $m_e \to -\infty$ by virtue of the stiffness reactance dominating. At resonance $m_e = 0$, and above it, the mass reactance dominates. The frequency of the driving force must be restricted in accordance with the inequality in §19.

23. INFLUENCE OF DAMPING   When the system of Fig. 16.1 is driven by a force $f \sin \omega t$ applied to m, by §§16, 19, the D.E. is

$$\ddot{x} + 2\kappa\dot{x} + \omega_1^2 x = f_1 \sin \omega t. \qquad 23.1$$

In virtue of damping, the displacement given by the complementary function of 23.1 is negligible soon after application of the driving force (see §§16.17). To determine the particular

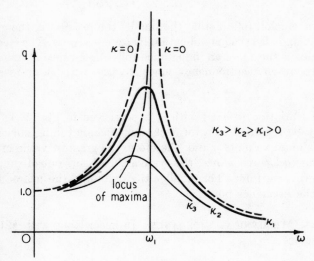

Fig. 23.1

integral and, therefore, the expression for the forced oscillation, we proceed as in §19, and find that

$$A = f\varphi^2/m(\varphi^4 + 4\kappa^2\omega^2), \qquad B = -2\kappa\omega A/\varphi^2, \qquad 23.2$$

where $\varphi^2 = (\omega_1^2 - \omega^2)$. Thus

$$x = (A^2 + B^2)^{1/2} \sin \{\omega t + \tan^{-1} (B/A)\} \qquad 23.3$$

$$= \frac{(f/m\omega_1^2) \sin (\omega t + \phi)}{\{[1 - (\omega/\omega_1)^2]^2 + 4\kappa^2\omega^2/\omega_1^4\}^{1/2}}, \qquad 23.4$$

with $\phi = \tan^{-1} 2\kappa\omega/(\omega^2 - \omega_1^2)$. Now $s = m\omega_1^2$, and $f/s = x_s$ the statical displacement corresponding to a constant force f. Thus we may write

$$x_{max} = x_s q, \qquad 23.5$$

where $q = 1/\{[1 - (\omega/\omega_1)^2]^2 + 4\kappa^2\omega^2/\omega_1^4\}^{1/2}$ is termed the *mag-*

nification factor [5, 22]. It is the ratio of the maximum vibrational to the statical displacement. At resonance $\omega = \omega_1$, and

$$x_{max} = x_s(\omega_1/2\kappa) = x_s(\omega_1 m/r), \qquad 23.6$$

from which it follows that the smaller the resistance, the greater x_{max} , and also the magnification factor $q = \omega_1 m/r$. The electrical analog is the 'Q' of an inductance coil of resistance R (measured at the resonance frequency, since R varies with ω), and we have

$$Q = \omega_1 L/R. \qquad 23.7$$

The variation in $q\,(Q)$ with ω is portrayed in Fig. 23.1, which may be regarded as a form of resonance or tuning curve. The maximum value of q and, therefore, the greatest value of x_{max} , occurs *below* resonance, the system then being out of tune with the driving force. The smaller the damping, the nearer is q_{max} to the resonance point.

24. MECHANICAL IMPEDANCE   In accordance with §21, 23.1 becomes

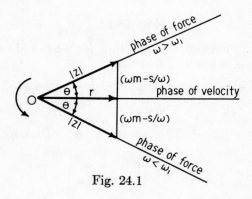

Fig. 24.1

$$m\dot{v} + rv + s \int^t v\, dt = fe^{i\omega t}, \qquad 24.1$$

so with $v = v_1 e^{i\omega t}$, we get

$$i\omega m v_1 + rv_1 + sv_1/i\omega = f, \qquad 24.2$$

and, therefore, the impedance presented to the driving agent at m is,

$$z = f/v_1 = r + i(\omega m - s/\omega) \qquad 24.3$$

$$= r + i\omega m\{1 - (\omega_1/\omega)^2\}. \qquad 24.4$$

Thus the impedance is a complex quantity, whose real part is the resistance r, and imaginary part the reactance $(\omega m - s/\omega)$, the latter being identical with that of the loss-free system in §21. z may be represented vectorially as in Fig. 24.1, where the cases $\omega < \omega_1$, $\omega > \omega_1$, i.e. below and above resonance, are shown. Resonance occurs when the reactance vanishes, so $\omega m = s/\omega$, and $z = r$, the impedance being entirely resistive. As stated in §23, the displacement does *not* have its greatest value then.

24.3, 24.4 may be expressed in the form

$$z = r + i\omega m_e, \qquad 24.5$$

where the effective mass $m_e = (m - s/\omega^2) = m\{1 - (\omega_1/\omega)^2\}$, being the same as that in §22. The modulus or absolute value of z is sometimes required, and by 24.3, 24.4

$$|z| = \{r^2 + (\omega m - s/\omega)^2\}^{1/2}$$
$$= \{r^2 + \omega^2 m^2[1 - (\omega_1/\omega)^2]^2\}^{1/2}. \qquad 24.6$$

The absolute value of the velocity is $f/|z|$.

For torsional vibrations, the formula corresponding to 24.3 is obtained by adding σ to the numerator of 21.8 (see 18.3).

25. ENERGY CONSIDERATIONS   The D.E. for the driven dissipative system is

$$m\ddot{x} + r\dot{x} + sx = f \sin \omega t. \qquad 25.1$$

Writing $dx/dt = v$, $d^2x/dt^2 = (dv/dx)(dx/dt) = v\, dv/dx$, 25.1 becomes

$$mv\, dv/dx + rv + sx = f \sin \omega t. \qquad 25.2$$

Multiplying throughout by $dx = v\,dt$ and integrating, gives

$$m \int v\,dv + r \int v^2\,dt + s \int x\,dx = f \int v \sin \omega t\,dt, \qquad 25.3$$

so $\qquad (mv^2 + sx^2)/2 + r \int v^2\,dt = f \int v \sin \omega t\,dt. \qquad 25.4$

Over a period $(0, 2\pi/\omega)$, the first term in 25.4 vanishes by virtue

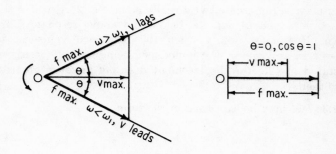

Fig. 25.1

of periodicity. To evaluate the integrals in 25.4, from 23.4 we have

$$v = dx/dt = \omega x_{max} \sin(\omega t + \theta), \qquad 25.5$$

where $\theta = (\pi/2 + \phi) = \tan^{-1}(\omega_1^2 - \omega^2)/2\kappa\omega$. Substituting for v into 25.4, we get

$$\omega^2 x_{max}^2 r \int_0^{2\pi/\omega} \sin^2(\omega t + \theta)\,dt$$

$$= f\omega x_{max} \int_0^{2\pi/\omega} \sin(\omega t + \theta) \sin \omega t\,dt, \qquad 25.6$$

so $\qquad \pi\omega x_{max}^2 r = \pi f x_{max} \cos\theta, \qquad 25.7$

or $\quad$ energy loss per period = energy supplied by driver p.p.

The power loss, or energy dissipated per unit time, is

$$P = \pi\omega x_{max}^2 r/(2\pi/\omega) = \omega^2 x_{max}^2 r/2 \qquad 25.8$$

$$= v_{max}^2 r/2 \sim I_{max}^2 R/2, \qquad 25.9$$

in an electrical circuit. In terms of f, the r.h.s. of 25.7 gives

$$P = \pi f x_{max} \cos\theta/(2\pi/\omega) = (f v_{max} \cos\theta)/2 \qquad 25.10$$

$$\sim (E_{max} I_{max} \cos\theta)/2, \qquad 25.11$$

in an electrical circuit. $\cos\theta = \cos\{\tan^{-1}(\omega_1^2 - \omega^2)/2\kappa\omega\} = 2\kappa\omega/\{(\omega_1^2 - \omega^2)^2 + 4\kappa^2\omega^2\}^{1/2}$, is called the *power factor* of the system, θ being the phase angle between force and velocity (see 25.1, 25.5). Below resonance $\omega < \omega_1$, $0 < \theta < \pi/2$, $1 > \cos\theta > 0$, and the phase of the velocity leads on that of the driving force.* Above resonance $\omega > \omega_1$, $-\pi/2 < \theta < 0$, $0 < \cos\theta < 1$, and the phase of the velocity lags on that of the driving force. At resonance $\omega = \omega_1$, $\theta = 0$, and $\cos\theta = 1$, i.e. unity power factor, the force and velocity being in phase, and the loss for a given f is nearly a maximum.† These aspects are illustrated vectorially in Fig. 25.1. The phase difference between v and f is due to stiffness reactance below resonance, and to mass reactance above it. At resonance the reactance vanishes, v and f are in phase, $\theta = 0$, and by 23.4, 25.5

$$v = f/r \sim I = E/R, \qquad 25.12$$

so we obtain the mechanical analog of Ohm's law.

From Fig. 25.1, it is seen that 25.10 is half the vector product (scalar or dot) of force and maximum velocity. If root mean square values are taken, $P = f_{r.m.s.} \, v_{r.m.s.} \, \cos\theta$, i.e. the vector product.

---

*The phase of f is used as a datum for that of v.

†By §23 the greatest value of x_{max} occurs below resonance. It is left as an exercise for the reader to show that the power loss attains a maximum when $\omega^2 = (\omega_1^2\alpha/3)\{1 + (1 + 3/\alpha^2)^{1/2}\} < \omega_1^2$, with $\alpha = (1 - 2\kappa^2/\omega_1^2)$. If $2\kappa^2/\omega_1^2 = r^2/2ms \ll 1$, then $\omega \simeq \omega_1$.

26. ELECTROMECHANICAL SYSTEM   Fig. 26.1A is a simplified schematic diagram of a cone loudspeaker. The driving coil is constrained by a centering spider (not shown) and an outer surround on the cone, to move axially in a radial magnetic field, which we shall assume to be uniform *along* the coil axis. The force on the coil due to a current I in it, is $\mathbf{C}I$, where $\mathbf{C}$* is the electromagnetic force factor. Assuming coil and cone to move bodily at *low* audio frequencies when driven by alternating current from an external source, we take m, r, s, to be mass,

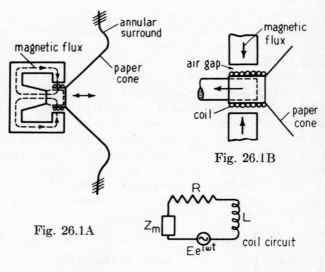

Fig. 26.1B

Fig. 26.1A

Fig. 26.1C

resistance, and stiffness, respectively, i.e. we consider the mechanical system to be a discrete type having one freedom.

There are two parts to be dealt with (i) electrical, (ii) mechanical. If the coil is displaced from its equilibrium position

---

*$\mathbf{C}$ is the product of magnetic flux density and length of wire on the coil. It is also the force on the coil per unit current, and this is equal to the e.m.f. induced in the coil per unit velocity, in virtue of its motion in the magnetic field.

and released, it executes a damped oscillation (see Fig. 17.1A) when open-circuited, and the system is a purely mechanical one. By short-circuiting the coil on itself, the damping is greater than before, owing to the current induced in virtue of the magnetic field, for by Lenz' law the motion is opposed. This shows that a coupling exists between the electrical and mechanical parts of the system, so long as the coil circuit is closed. The induced e.m.f. is $\mathbf{C}v = \mathbf{C}d\xi/dt$.

For (i) the sum of the internal must equal the external e.m.f., so

$$L\,dI/dt + RI + \mathbf{C}d\xi/dt = Ee^{i\omega t}, \qquad 26.1$$

where L, R, ξ are inductance, resistance, and displacement, respectively.

For (ii) the sum of the internal must equal the external force, so

$$md^2\xi/dt^2 + rd\xi/dt + s\xi = \mathbf{C}I. \qquad 26.2$$

To obtain the forced oscillation we may replace d/dt by $i\omega e^{i\omega t}$, so the D.E. become

$$(R + i\omega L)I + i\omega \mathbf{C}\xi = E, \qquad 26.3$$

and $\qquad (s - \omega^2 m + i\omega r)\xi = \mathbf{C}I. \qquad 26.4$

From 26.4

$$\xi = \mathbf{C}I/(s - \omega^2 m + i\omega r), \qquad 26.5$$

and on substituting into 26.3, we get [10]

$$E = I\{(R + i\omega L) + \mathbf{C}^2/[r + i(\omega m - s/\omega)]\}. \qquad 26.6$$

Hence the electrical impedance of the circuit is

$$E/I = (R + i\omega L) + \frac{\mathbf{C}^2[r + i(s/\omega - \omega m)]}{r^2 + (s/\omega - \omega m)^2} \qquad 26.7$$

$$= R + r\mathbf{C}^2/|z|^2 + i\omega\{L + \mathbf{C}^2(s/\omega^2 - m)/|z|^2\}, \qquad 26.8$$

where by 24.6, $|z|$ is the absolute value of the mechanical impedance of the system. When the coil is *clamped*, the electrical impedance is $Z = R + i\omega L$, so by 26.8 the total impedance *during motion* is

$$Z + Z_m = (R + R_m) + i\omega(L + L_m). \qquad 26.9$$

Hence in virtue of the electromagnetic coupling, there is a motional resistance R_m, and a motional inductance L_m, both of which vary with ω. The motional impedance is $Z_m = R_m + i\omega L_m$.

From 26.6 we also have [10]

$$Z_m = \mathbf{C}^2/[r + i(\omega m - s/\omega)] = \mathbf{C}^2/z, \qquad 26.10$$

so
$$\mathbf{C}^2 = zZ_m, \qquad 26.11$$

the product of the mechanical and electrical motional impedances, which may be regarded as the coupling factor. Mechanical resonance occurs when $s/\omega = \omega m$ or $\omega^2 = s/m$, and then

$$Z_m = \mathbf{C}^2/r, \qquad L_m = 0, \qquad 26.12$$

the mechanical impedance being purely resistive. Electrical resonance occurs when $L + L_m = 0$, so by 26.8

$$|z|^2 L + \mathbf{C}^2(s/\omega^2 - m) = 0, \qquad 26.13$$

from which we find that, provided r^2 is negligible,

$$\omega^2 = (s/m) + (\mathbf{C}^2/mL), \qquad 26.14$$

which exceeds the value for mechanical resonance. If s can be made small enough, 26.14 gives

$$\omega^2 \simeq \mathbf{C}^2/mL, \qquad 26.15$$

from which it follows that the 'stiffness' is provided by the electromagnetic coupling, and the system oscillates without mechanical constraint!

★27. EQUIVALENT ELECTRICAL CIRCUITS [10] So far as the driving e.m.f. is concerned, the loudspeaker may be replaced by the *equivalent* series circuit of Fig. 27.1A, where R_m, L_m, both vary with ω. Since $L_m = \mathbf{C}^2(s/\omega^2 - m)/|z|^2$, it is positive below, zero at, and negative above mechanical resonance.

$R_m = r\mathbf{C}^2/[r^2 + (s/\omega - \omega m)^2]$, and this attains a maximum value at mechanical resonance, where $s/\omega = \omega m$, and $R_m = \mathbf{C}^2/r$. Hence the smaller is r, the greater the motional resistance, and in practice the current falls to a relatively low value, since $R_m \gg R$.

The series circuit of Fig. 27.1A may be replaced by one in which the components of the motional impedance are in parallel,

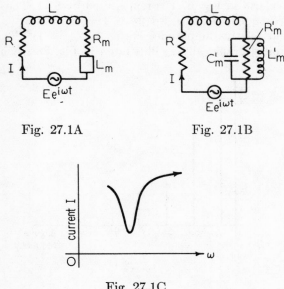

Fig. 27.1A   Fig. 27.1B

Fig. 27.1C

as shown in Fig. 27.1B. Here $R'_m = \mathbf{C}^2/r$, $L'_m = \mathbf{C}^2/s$, $C'_m = m/\mathbf{C}^2$, all of these being *independent* of ω. It may be remarked that Fig. 27.1B is *not* an analog, because L'_m, C'_m, pertain to stiffness and mass, respectively, which is the other way round from the analog. At mechanical resonance $\omega = (s/m)^{1/2} = I/(L'_m C'_m)^{1/2}$, this being the resonant frequency of the inductance and capacitance. Their combined impedance is now infinite, so the circuital impedance becomes $Z = (R + R'_m) + i\omega L$. In practice $i\omega L$ is usually negligible, so the impedance Z is almost purely resistive, and with r small enough, Z may be very large. The current-frequency curve has a crevasse, as illustrated in Fig. 27.1C.

28. FREQUENCY SPECTRA   By Fourier's theorem, any repeated waveform $f(t)$—with certain restrictions—may be represented by an infinite set of *discrete* components of different frequencies, whose amplitudes depend upon $f(t)$. For instance, the waveform in Fig. 67.1 is represented by 67.1. The discrete angular frequencies are $\omega_n = (2n - 1)\pi c/2l$, $n = 1, 2, 3, \cdots$, and their relative amplitudes are as $1/(2n - 1)^2$. They may be exhibited graphically as illustrated in Fig. 28.1, which is a

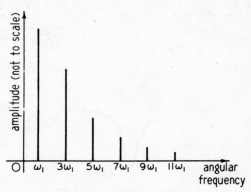

Fig. 28.1

discrete or *line* spectrum. When, however, $f(t)$ is not repeated—and is usually of short duration—e.g. the zeroth period in Fig. 67.1 from O to D, Fourier's *integral* theorem shows that the triangular 'impulse' may be represented by a *band* or continuous frequency spectrum the range being $\omega = (0, +\infty)$. Using Re to denote the real part, by the integral theorem—provided certain conditions are satisfied—

$$f(t) = (1/\pi)Re\left\{\int_0^\infty e^{i\omega t}\, d\omega \int_{-\infty}^\infty e^{-i\omega x} f(x)\, dx\right\}, \qquad 28.1$$

where
$$F(i\omega) = \int_{-\infty}^{\infty} e^{-i\omega x} f(x) \, dx \qquad 28.2$$

is defined to be the *Fourier transform* of $f(x)$. $|F(i\omega)|$ is an index of the relative amplitudes of the angular frequencies ω, which constitute the band spectrum of $f(t)$. When these are summed—in the appropriate way—we obtain

$$f(t) = (1/\pi)Re\left\{\int_{0}^{\infty} e^{i\omega t} F(i\omega) \, d\omega\right\}, \qquad 28.3$$

so the original function is reproduced.

29. RECTANGULAR IMPULSE This is shown in Fig. 29.1, where the ordinate is force or its analog, and the area $\int_{0}^{h} f \, dt =$

Fig. 29.1

$fh = S$ is the *strength* of the impulse, which we shall suppose constant, so that $f = S/h$. For a mechanical system the units of S are force $\times$ time or mass $\times$ velocity, i.e. momentum, mlt^{-1}. The electrical analog is voltage $\times$ time. By 28.2

$$F(i\omega) = (S/h) \int_{0}^{h} e^{-i\omega x} \, dx = (iS/\omega h)(e^{-i\omega h} - 1), \qquad 29.1$$

the limits $(0, h)$ being used, since $f(x)$ is zero outside this range. Thus

$$F(i\omega) = (S/\omega h)\{\sin \omega h + i(\cos \omega h - 1)\}, \qquad 29.2$$

and after a little reduction, we get

$$|F(i\omega)| = S |\sin (\omega h/2)|/(\omega h/2). \qquad 29.3$$

Graphs of 29.3 for (a) h small, and (b) $h \to 0$ are shown in

Fig. 29.2. They represent the band or continuous spectra for the impulses. When $h \to 0$, $f \to +\infty$, so the impulse has infinite am-

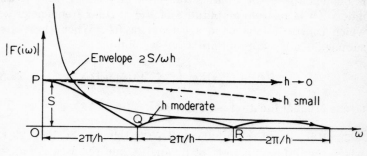

Fig. 29.2

plitude but finite strength S nevertheless! In (a) the amplitude is variable and has zeros at interval $2\pi/h$, but in (b) as $h \to 0$, the interval $\to +\infty$, while $|F(i\omega)| \to S$ for all ω in $(0, +\infty)$. Hence the impulse of infinite amplitude but strength S, has a *uniform* frequency spectrum. It is convenient to employ the symbol $I(t)$ to represent an infinite impulse of *unit* strength [13].

In practice infinite impulses are out of the question, but as we shall see later, the concept may be put to good use analytically. It often gives an adequate approximation to a large force f having a short duration h.

30. APPLICATION OF IMPULSE TO SYSTEM OF FIG. 2.1A   The impulse in Fig. 29.1 may be defined as follows [13]

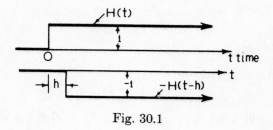

Fig. 30.1

$$f(t) = f, \quad 0 < t < h \atop = 0, \quad t < 0, t > h \Bigg\} = f\{H(t) - H(t - h)\}, \qquad 30.1$$

where $H(t)$ is Heavisides' unit or step function, which is zero when $t < 0$, unity when $t > 0$, but *discontinuous and undefined* at $t = 0$ (Fig. 30.1). The D.E. for the system is

$$m\ddot{x} + sx = f\{H(t) - H(t - h)\}, \qquad 30.2$$

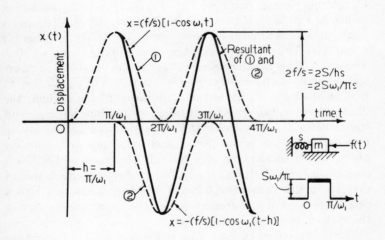

Fig. 30.2.

or $\qquad \ddot{x} + \omega_1^2 x = (f/m)\{H(t) - H(t - h)\}. \qquad 30.3$

To solve 30.3 we shall use operational calculus based upon the p-multiplied Laplace transform [13], where $p \int_0^\infty e^{-pt} x(t) \, dt = \phi(p)$, which for brevity we write $x(t) \Rightarrow \phi(p)$. Then the transform equation for 30.3 is

$$(p^2 + \omega_1^2)\phi = (f/m)(1 - e^{-ph}), \qquad 30.4$$

so $\qquad \phi = (f/m)\{1/(p^2 + \omega_1^2) - e^{-ph}/(p^2 + \omega_1^2)\}. \qquad 30.5$

Using a list of L.T.S., the inverse transform or interpretation of 30.5 is, with $s = \omega_1^2 m$,

$$x(t) = (f/s)(1 - \cos \omega_1 t), \qquad 0 < t < h, \qquad 30.6$$

and $\quad x(t) = (f/s)\{[1 - \cos \omega_1 t] - [1 - \cos \omega_1(t - h)]\}, \quad 30.7$

in $h < t < +\infty$. The solutions pertaining to the above intervals are different, because $H(t - h) = 0$ in the first interval.

The graph of $x(t)$ for the second interval may be obtained by plotting the two parts in [   ] in 30.7, and subtracting, as shown in Fig. 30.2. If $h \to +\infty$ in Fig. 29.1, $f(t) = fH(t)$ and a constant force is applied to the system at $t = 0$. The solution for $t > 0$ is 30.6, the displacement-time graph being ① in Fig. 30.2. The mean or average displacement is f/s, and upon this is superimposed a harmonic motion $-(f/s) \cos \omega_1 t$. When $-fH(t - h)$ is applied at $t = h$, by virtue of linearity of the system, the displacement curve ② is identical in shape, but reversed and commencing at $t = h$. Hence the constant terms cancel, leaving two oscillations of equal period and amplitude but different phase, which combine to give the full line curve of Fig. 30.2, starting at $t = h$. Although the spectrum of the impulse is spread over an infinite frequency band, it has been converted into a single line spectrum of frequency ω_1, the natural frequency of the system, in virtue of selectivity.

The displacement of the spring at $t = \pi/\omega$ is $2f/s$, being *twice* the statical value. The same effect is obtained if a uniform bar, fixed at one end, is pulled suddenly at its free end by a constant force. The condition to be satisfied is that the work done by f in causing a displacement x is equal to the potential energy stored in the spring. Hence we must have $fx = sx^2/2$, so $x = 2f/s$.

31. INFLUENCE OF DURATION OF IMPULSE   Prior to $t = h$, the displacement is given by 30.6, which is represented by curve ① in Fig. 30.2. If $h = 2\pi/\omega_1$, $4\pi/\omega_1$, etc., x and $\dot{x}$ are zero, so the system is quiescent, and it will remain in this condition if f be removed then.

30.7 may be written

$$x(t) = \{(S/\omega_1 m)/(\omega_1 h/2)\} \sin (\omega_1 h/2) \sin \omega_1 (t - h/2), \quad 31.1$$

where $f = S/h$, and $\omega_1^2 m = s$. When $\sin (\omega_1 h/2) = 0$, i.e. $h = 2n\pi/\omega_1$, $x(t) = 0$ in $h < t < +\infty$, which is the analytical version of the previous paragraph. With $n = 1$, $x(t)$ would be curve ① in Fig. 30.2 from $t = 0$ to $2\pi/\omega_1$, and zero thereafter.

Limiting case $h \to 0$. Then $\sin (\omega_1 h/2) \to \omega_1 h/2$ and 31.1 degenerates to

$$x(t) = (S/\omega_1 m) \sin \omega_1 t. \qquad 31.2$$

Thus in virtue of the selectivity of the dynamical system, the *uniform* band spectrum of the infinite impulse has been transformed to a single line spectrum at frequency ω_1. The energy supplied by the impulse is

$$T = m v_{\max}^2/2 = S^2/2m, \qquad 31.3$$

and it increases inversely with m.

Viscous damping. The response to the impulse $SI(t)$ will then be a decay transient. The D.E. is 23.1 with $(f/m) \sin \omega t$ replaced by $(S/m)I(t)$, so we get

$$\ddot{x} + 2\kappa\dot{x} + \omega_1^2 x = (S/m)I(t), \qquad 31.4$$

whose transform equation is

$$(p^2 + 2\kappa p + \omega_1^2)\phi = (S/m)p, \qquad 31.5$$

where $I(t) \rightleftharpoons p$. Taking $\omega_1 > \kappa = r/2m$, which corresponds to an oscillatory system, we have

$$\phi = (S/m)p/\{(p + \kappa)^2 + (\omega_1^2 - \kappa^2)\}, \qquad 31.6$$

of which the inverse transform is

$$x(t) = \{S/m(\omega_1^2 - \kappa^2)^{1/2}\}e^{-\kappa t} \sin (\omega_1^2 - \kappa^2)^{1/2}t. \qquad 31.7$$

31.7 represents an exponentially damped sinusoidal oscillation.

If $\kappa = 0$, the formula degenerates to 31.2, as we should expect. The energy supplied by the impulse is independent of both κ

and *s*, because it is transferred at $t = 0$, before the system starts to move (from an analytical viewpoint), so there is neither displacement nor energy loss. To corroborate this statement, the energy may be calculated from

$$\int_0^\infty v^2 r \, dt \sim \int_0^\infty I^2 R \, dt \qquad 31.8$$

for an electrical circuit. Then by aid of 31.7, the integral to be evaluated is

$$\{r(\omega_1 S/m\alpha)^2/2\} \int_0^\infty e^{-2\kappa t} \{1 + \cos 2(\alpha t + \beta)\} \, dt, \qquad 31.9$$

with $\alpha = (\omega_1^2 - \kappa^2)^{1/2}$, $\beta = \tan^{-1}(\kappa/\alpha)$. The result is $S^2/2m$ as at 31.3, which is independent of κ and s, as stated above.

★*Frequency spectrum derived from Laplace transform.* The exponentially damped sine wave has a band spectrum given by $|\{\phi(p)/p\}_{p=i\omega}|$. Thus by 31.5

$$F(i\omega = \{\phi(p)/p\}_{p=i\omega}$$
$$= (S/m)/\{(\omega_1^2 - \omega^2) + 2i\kappa\omega\}, \qquad 31.10$$

so $\qquad | F(i\omega) | = (S/m)/\{(\omega_1^2 - \omega^2)^2 + 4\kappa^2\omega^2\}^{1/2}. \qquad 31.11$

The r.h.s. of 31.11 is a *continuous* function of ω in $(0, +\infty)$, which should be graphed by the reader. The spectrum of the rectangular impulse in §29 may be derived by the above procedure. The latter is valid provided integral 28.2 converges uniformly in the infinite range $\omega = (0, +\infty)$, when the lower limit is zero. The *uniform* convergence entails a *continuous* spectrum. In some cases the integral may diverge, but the spectrum can often be found by a limiting process. For instance

$$\int_0^\infty e^{-i\omega x} \, dx \qquad 31.12$$

which corresponds to $H(t)$, is divergent. Now for all practical purposes if $\mu > 0$, but *extremely* small, $e^{-\mu t}H(t) \simeq H(t)$. Then by 28.2

$$F(i\omega + \mu) = \int_0^\infty e^{-(i\omega + \mu)x} \, dx = 1/(i\omega + \mu), \qquad 31.13$$

so $\quad | F(i\omega + \mu) | = 1/(\omega^2 + \mu^2)^{1/2}.$ $\qquad\qquad\qquad$ 31.14

As $\mu \to 0$, $| F(i\omega + \mu) | \to \omega^{-1}$, which gives the spectrum of $H(t)$ *considered to be a limiting case.* The index in 31.13 may be written $-i(\omega - i\mu)x$, so we have introduced a complex or generalised angular frequency. Thus to derive the spectrum in cases of the above type, divide the p-multiplied L.T. by p, then substitute $(i\omega + \mu)$ for p, calculate the modulus and let $\mu \to 0$. In effect $H(t)$ has a line spectrum at $\omega = 0$, which causes a statical displacement, provided the system has stiffness, which may be discrete or distributed continuously.

Since the L.T. is for the range $t = (0, +\infty)$, whereas in 28.2 the range corresponds to $t = (-\infty, +\infty)$, 31.10 gives the *half-range* Fourier transform.

When a force of arbitrary waveform (expressed as a function of t) is applied suddenly (at $t = 0$) to a system having $n \geq 1$ degrees of freedom, the n natural frequencies are excited, if the spectrum of the force contains these frequencies. This would certainly be the case with a continuous spectrum devoid of zeros. The relative amplitudes of the natural vibrations depend upon the initial displacement and velocity of the system, and also upon the spectrum. The first paragraph of §31 gives an instance where the spectrum has a zero corresponding to the natural frequency of the system, and after an interval $2n\pi/\omega_1$ the motion ceases.

CHAPTER III

Non-Linear Systems having One Degree of Freedom

32. INTRODUCTION The D.E. with which we have been concerned hitherto, were linear in type, because the 'characteristic' relationships, e.g. $f = sx$, were linear in x. In a linear D.E. the *dependent* variable occurs to the first power only. A term involving x^2, x^3, $x^{1/2}$, would render the equation non-linear. For instance

$$m\ddot{x} + s_1 x + s_3 x^3 = 0 \qquad 32.1$$

is non-linear. Although of the second order in x, this equation has only one solution, and it cannot be multiplied by an arbi-

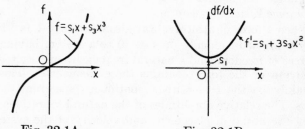

Fig. 32.1A   Fig. 32.1B

trary constant. To determine x for a given set of initial conditions, two integrations are needed, thereby obtaining two constants, and these are functions of the initial conditions. The vibrational frequency of a loss-free non-linear system depends upon the displacement and velocity *at* $t = 0$. This is in marked contrast with a linear system ($s_3 = 0$), for which the D.E. has two linearly independent solutions, each of which may be multiplied by an arbitrary constant, and then added.

In 32.1, the 'characteristic' of the system is $f = s_1 x + s_3 x^3$. It is an odd function of x, since $f(x) = -f(-x)$, and the graph is anti-symmetrical about the f-axis, as illustrated in Fig. 32.1A. The stiffness is defined to be $df/dx = s_1 + 3s_3x^2$, being parabolic in form (see Fig. 32.1B), and not constant, as in a linear system where $df/dx = s$. A characteristic of the above type may occur in various devices. When $s_3 > 0$, it can be obtained by the arrangement shown schematically in Fig. 32.2. A thin bar is clamped between shaped blocks, so that the 'bending' length decreases with increase in x. By using suitably shaped blocks, the relationship $f = s_1x + s_3x^3$ may be obtained to an adequate degree of approximation. Suppose a mass m is fixed

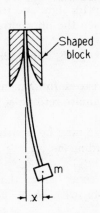

Shaped
block

m

x

Fig. 32.2.

at the free end of the bar and displaced by x_0 . In absence of loss, on being released the system will execute periodic vibrations of amplitude x_0 , about the equilibrium position. The frequency is a function of x_0 (see 33.10), whereas in a linear system this is not so, e.g. in §3, $\omega_1 = (s/m)^{1/2}$.

33. SOLUTION OF 32.1   The D.E. may be written

$$\ddot{x} + \alpha x + \beta x^3 = 0,\qquad\qquad 33.1$$

where $\alpha = s_1/m$, $\beta = s_3/m$. This can be solved *exactly* by means of an elliptic integral, or approximately by iteration, perturbation, or Fourier series, since the motion is periodic. Choosing the latter, we assume that

$$x = a_0 + \sum_{r=1}^{\infty} a_r \sin r\omega t + \sum_{r=1}^{\infty} b_r \cos r\omega t. \qquad 33.2$$

For initial conditions we shall take $x = x_0$, $\dot{x} = 0$, $t = 0$. The motion is symmetrical about the central position $x = 0$, so there is no unidirectional displacement, and $a_0 = 0$. Inserting the second condition, all the a_r vanish, so the second sigma term alone remains. Now x in each quarter period of the oscillation is identical, except for sign, and this precludes terms of the type $b_{2r} \cos 2r\omega t$. Hence the appropriate form of solution is

$$x(t) = \sum_{r=0}^{\infty} b_{2r+1} \cos (2r + 1)\omega t, \qquad 33.3$$

so the motion comprises a fundamental vibration of angular frequency ω, and an infinite retinue of harmonics of frequencies $3\omega, 5\omega, \cdots$

In 33.1, $\alpha > 0$, but β may be positive or negative. If $\beta < 0$, $\alpha x + \beta x^3 \leq 0$ according as $|x| \geq (\alpha/|\beta|)^{1/2}$, so to avoid instability $|x| < (\alpha/|\beta|)^{1/2}$.

Assuming, for the time being, that $|b_5|$, $|b_7|$, $\cdots$, are negligible in comparison with $|b_1|$, $|b_3|$, as a first approximation we take

$$x \simeq b_1 \cos \omega t + b_3 \cos 3\omega t. \qquad 33.4$$

Substituting into 33.1, we obtain

$$\ddot{x} = -\omega^2(b_1 \cos \omega t + 9b_3 \cos 3\omega t) \qquad 33.5$$

$$\alpha x = \alpha(b_1 \cos \omega t + b_3 \cos 3\omega t) \qquad 33.6$$

$$\left. \begin{aligned} \beta x^3 = (\beta/4)\{ & b_1^3(3 \cos \omega t + \cos 3\omega t) + 6b_1^2 b_3 \cos 3\omega t \\ & + 3b_1^2 b_3(\cos \omega t + \cos 5\omega t) + 6b_1 b_3^2 \cos \omega t \\ & + 3b_1 b_3^2(\cos 5\omega t + \cos 7\omega t) \\ & + b_3^3(3 \cos 3\omega t + \cos 9\omega t) \}. \end{aligned} \right\} \qquad 33.7$$

Since the assumed solution 33.4 has no terms in cos $5\omega t$, cos $7\omega t$, cos $9\omega t$, they will be omitted from 33.7. The additional assumption that $|\, b_3\,| \ll |\, b_1\,|$ permits neglect of terms involving b_3^2, b_3^3, so we take 33.7 in the form

$$\beta x^3 = (3\beta b_1^2/4)(b_1 + b_3) \cos \omega t + (\beta b_1^2/4)(b_1 + 6b_3) \cos 3\omega t. \qquad 33.8$$

Now by 33.1 the coefficient of cos ωt must vanish, so from 33.5, 33.6, 33.8 we get

$$-\omega^2 b_1 + \alpha b_1 + (3\beta b_1^2/4)(b_1 + b_3) = 0, \qquad 33.9$$

or
$$\omega^2 = \alpha + 3\beta b_1 x_0/4, \qquad 33.10$$

where $x_0 = (b_1 + b_3)$. 33.10 shows that ω depends upon the amplitude of the motion x_0. The greater x_0, the higher the angular frequency, and the shorter the period of the oscillation, so that the motion is not isochronous.* From a physical viewpoint this follows from the fact that the control stiffness $s_1 + 3s_3 x^2$ increases with increase in amplitude. If x_0 is very small and $3s_3 x_0^2 \ll s$, 33.10 gives

$$\omega^2 \simeq \alpha = s_1/m, \qquad 33.11$$

as in the linear case in §3.

To determine b_1, b_3, we proceed thus: Equating the coefficient of cos $3\omega t$ from 33.5, 33.6, 33.8, to zero,

$$-9\omega^2 b_3 + \alpha b_3 + b_1^2(b_1 + 6b_3)/4 = 0. \qquad 33.12$$

Substituting for ω^2 from 33.10 and omitting the term in b_3^2, we get

$$b_3 \simeq \beta b_1^3/(32\alpha + 21\beta b_1^2), \qquad 33.13$$

so
$$b_3/b_1 \simeq 1/\{21 + (32\alpha/\beta b_1^2)\} \qquad 33.14$$

$$= \varphi \ll 1, \qquad 33.15$$

provided α, β are positive. Hence the assumption that $b_3 \ll b_1$

---

*Independent of amplitude.

is justifiable. It may also be shown that terms involving b_5, b_7, $\cdots$, are negligible.

Since $b_3 \simeq \varphi b_1$, and $x_0 = (b_1 + b_3)$, it follows that

$$b_1 \simeq (1 - \varphi)x_0\,, \qquad \text{and} \qquad b_3 \simeq \varphi(1 - \varphi)x_0\,. \qquad 33.16$$

Substituting from 33.16 into 33.4 yields the approximate solution

$$x = x_0(1 - \varphi)\{\cos \omega t + \varphi \cos 3\omega t\}. \qquad 33.17$$

From this we infer that although the extent of the non-linearity is unrestricted (s_1, s_3 may have any real positive values), *the motion is nearly harmonic*. The amplitude of the third harmonic is less than 5 per cent that of the fundamental. If the initial conditions were $x = x_0$, $\dot{x} = x_1$, by virtue of momentum at the start, the amplitude of m at the end of the first swing to the left would be $x_{max} > x_0$. Thereafter the motion would be represented by 33.17 with x_{max} for x_0, t now being measured from the commencement of the swing to the right. The determination of x_{max} remains as an exercise for the reader.

★34. EQUIVALENT LINEAR SYSTEM   In virtue of the almost harmonic nature of the motion, the system is approximately equivalent to the linear type whose equation is

$$m\ddot{x} + m\omega_1^2 x = 0, \qquad \text{or} \qquad \ddot{x} + \omega_1^2 x = 0, \qquad 34.1$$

m being as before, but the stiffness now approximately

$$s = m\omega_1^2 = m(\alpha + 3\beta b_1 x_0/4) \qquad 34.2$$

$$= s_1 + 3(1 - \varphi)s_3 x_0^2/4. \qquad 34.3$$

This is constant for a given initial displacement x_0.

35. SIMPLE PENDULUM   Referring to Fig. 35.1A, the D.E. is derived by equating the sum of the internal forces to zero. Thus

$$m(l\ddot{\theta}) + mg \sin \theta = 0. \qquad 35.1$$

Since $\sin \theta = \theta - \theta^3/6 + \cdots$, 35.1 is non-linear. If, however,

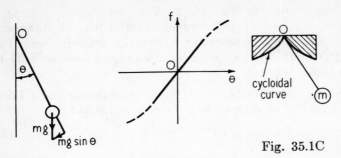

Fig. 35.1C

Fig. 35.1A   Fig. 35.1B

$|\theta| < \pi/6$, the approximation $\sin\theta = \theta - \theta^3/6$ may be used, so 35.1 becomes

$$\ddot{\theta} + (g/l)(\theta - \theta^3/6) = 0. \qquad 35.2$$

This has the same form as 33.1, with $\alpha = g/l$, $\beta = -(g/6l)$. Hence by 33.10

$$\omega^2 \simeq (g/l) - (gb_1\theta_0/8l) = (g/l)\{1 - (b_1\theta_0/8)\}. \qquad 35.3$$

In the present problem $\beta < 0$, and $\alpha/\beta = -6$, so 33.14 gives

$$b_3/b_1 \simeq 1/(21 - 192/b_1^2). \qquad 35.4$$

Now $|b_1| < \pi/6$, so $b_1^2 < \pi^2/36$ and, therefore, by 35.4

$$|b_3/b_1| < 1/\{(192 \times 36/\pi^2 - 21)\} \simeq 0.0015. \qquad 35.5$$

Thus $b_1 \simeq \theta_0$, and 35.3 becomes

$$\omega^2 \simeq (g/l)\{1 - (\theta_0^2/8)\}, \qquad 35.6$$

so the periodic time is

$$\tau = 2\pi/\omega \simeq 2\pi(l/g)^{1/2}(1 + \theta_0^2/16). \qquad 35.7$$

This expression shows that the motion is not isochronous, because the periodic time increases with increase in the amplitude of swing θ_0. The reduced rate of motion is caused by decrease in the slope of the control term $g(\theta - \theta^3/6)$ with increase in θ. This will be evident from the characteristic curve for the system, shown in Fig. 35.1B. The 'equivalent' stiffness is $df/d\theta = g(1 - \theta^2/2)$. Isochronous motion may be obtained if the cord moves between two cycloidally shaped blocks (Fig. 35.1C), so that as $|\theta|$ increases, l is reduced automatically by the correct amount.

36. FORCED OSCILLATIONS   We consider the system in §32 to be driven by an external force $f \sin \omega t$, so the D.E. is

$$m\ddot{x} + s_1 x + s_3 x^3 = f \sin \omega t, \qquad 36.1$$

or $$\ddot{x} + \alpha x + \beta x^3 = f_1 \sin \omega t. \qquad (f_1 = f/m) \qquad 36.2$$

We assume that there is a small amount of damping, so that a short time after application of the driving force the transient is negligible, and the motion periodic. Consequently the initial conditions need not be introduced. We assume also that the condition for a subharmonic is not satisfied. In virtue of considerations akin to those in §33, as a first approximation we take

$$x = a_1 \sin \omega t + a_3 \sin 3\omega t, \qquad 36.3$$

with $|a_3| \ll |a_1|$. Substituting into 36.2 and proceeding as in §33, we obtain

$$\ddot{x} = -\omega^2(a_1 \sin \omega t + 9a_3 \sin 3\omega t) \qquad 36.4$$

$$\alpha x = \alpha(a_1 \sin \omega t + a_3 \sin 3\omega t) \qquad 36.5$$

$$\beta x^3 = (\beta/4)\{3a_1^2(a_1 - a_3) \sin \omega t - a_1^2(a_1 - 6a_3) \sin 3\omega t\}, \qquad 36.6$$

terms in $\sin 5\omega t$, $\sin 7\omega t$, $\sin 9\omega t$, being omitted since they do not appear in 36.3.

Equating the coefficients of $\sin \omega t$ on both sides of 36.2 (using 36.4-36.6), yields

$$(\alpha - \omega^2)a_1 + (3\beta a_1^2/4)(a_1 - a_3) = f_1 , \qquad 36.7$$

so $$\omega^2 \simeq \alpha + 3\beta a_1^2/4 - f_1/a_1 , \qquad 36.8$$

which is an approximation to the amplitude-frequency relation. ω is dependent upon both a_1 and f_1 .

When $\beta = 0$, the system is linear, and 36.8 gives the exact relationship

$$a_1 = f_1/(\alpha - \omega^2), \qquad 36.9$$

as at 19.5, $\alpha = \omega_1^2$ being the natural frequency of the *linear* system.

36.8 may be written

$$3\beta a_1^3/4 + (\alpha - \omega^2)a_1 - f_1 = 0, \qquad 36.10$$

which is a cubic equation for a_1, when α, β, ω, f_1 are given. It has three roots, (i) all real, or (ii) one real and two complex conjugate. This aspect will be discussed later; meanwhile we shall investigate the assumption $|a_3| \ll |a_1|$.

Equating the coefficient of $\sin 3\omega t$ from 36.4-36.6 to zero,

we have $\qquad (\alpha - 9\omega^2)a_3 - \beta a_1^2(a_1 - 6a_3)/4 = 0, \qquad 36.11$

so $\qquad a_3 = \beta a_1^3/4(\alpha - 9\omega^2 + 3\beta a_1^2/2). \qquad 36.12$

Substituting for ω^2 from 36.8, leads to

$$a_3 = -\beta a_1^3/(21\beta a_1^2 + 32\alpha - 36f_1/a_1), \qquad 36.13$$

so $\qquad a_3/a_1 = -1/\{21 + (32\alpha - 36f_1/a_1)/\beta a_1^2\}. \qquad 36.14$

Hence $|a_3/a_1| \ll 1$, provided

$$|\, 21 + (32\alpha - 36f_1/a_1)/\beta a_1^2 \,| \gg 1. \qquad 36.15$$

It may be shown that terms involving a_5, a_7, $\cdots$, are negligible, so the motion is *almost harmonic*, the displacement of fundamental frequency being in phase with the driving force.

★37. EQUIVALENT LINEAR SYSTEM   When 36.15 is satisfied and the forced vibration is nearly harmonic, suppose we replace 36.2 by the *linear* D.E.

$$\ddot{x} + \omega_1^2 x = f_1 \sin \omega t, \qquad 37.1$$

where $\omega_1^2 = \alpha + 3\beta a_1^2/4$, a_1 being constant. Then 37.1 applies to the linear system of Fig. 2.1A when driven, and having natural frequency as above. The particular integral of 37.1 is

$$x = f_1 \sin \omega t/(\omega_1^2 - \omega^2).$$
  37.2

Since $|a_3/a_1| \ll 1$, $x_{max} \simeq a_1$, so 37.2 gives

$$a_1 \simeq f_1/(\alpha + 3\beta a_1^2/4 - \omega^2),$$
  37.3

or $\qquad \omega^2 \simeq \alpha + 3\beta a_1^2/4 - f_1/a_1 = \omega_1^2 - f_1/a_1,$
  37.4

as at 36.8. In the equivalent system, m is unaltered but

$$s = m\omega_1^2 \simeq m(\alpha + 3\beta a_1^2/4),$$
  37.5

which depends on a_1. The undamped non-linear system cannot resonate, for at resonance $\omega = \omega_1$, but by 37.4 this is impossible because $f_1/a_1 \neq 0$.

38. AMPLITUDE-FREQUENCY CURVES [6] The a-ω relationship is given at 36.8. First we take $f_1 = 0$ and plot

$$a_1 = \{(4/3\beta)(\omega^2 - \alpha)\}^{1/2},$$
  38.1

as shown by the broken line in Fig. 38.1A. This is the amplitude-frequency relationship for the 'free' vibrations (see 33.10). Next we plot

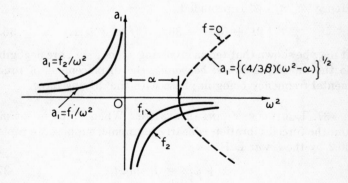

Fig. 38.1A

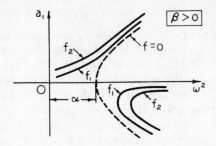

Fig. 38.1B

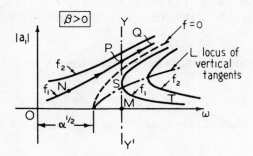

Fig. 38.1C

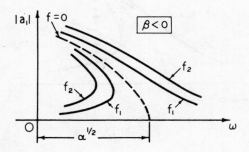

Fig. 38.1D

$$\omega^2 = -f_r/a_1, \quad \text{or} \quad a_1 = -f_r/\omega^2, \quad r = 1, 2, \cdots, \quad 38.2$$

for various values of $f_r^* > 0$, thereby obtaining the full line curves. The result of adding the abscissae of these curves is depicted in Fig. 38.1B, while in Fig. 38.1C, $|a_1|$ is plotted against ω. These are the amplitude-frequency curves. Consider that marked f_1. When ω is on the left of the vertical tangent $Y'Y$, a_1 in 36.10 has one real and two complex values. At $Y'Y$ there are three real values, two being coincident at S, while on the right of $Y'Y$, the three values are different. The amplitude-frequency curves for $\beta < 0$, are given in Fig. 38.1D, while those for $\beta = 0$ (the familiar resonance curves of a tuned system) are shown in Fig. 19.1A. The curves for $\beta > 0$, and $\beta < 0$, resemble those of Fig. 19.1A sheared over to the right and left, respectively.

39. Amplitude-frequency curves with damping [6] The D.E. is now

$$\ddot{x} + 2\kappa\dot{x} + \alpha x + \beta x^3 = f_1 \sin(\omega t + \varphi), \qquad 39.1$$

where the phase angle φ has been introduced for analytical

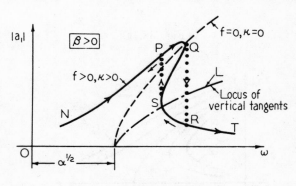

Fig. 39.1A

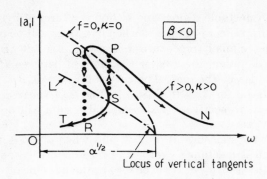

Fig. 39.1B

convenience, because the displacement and driving force are out
of phase owing to loss.* If we assume that

$$x = a_1 \sin \omega t + a_3 \sin 3\omega t, \qquad 39.2$$

and proceed as in §36, we obtain the relationship

$$\{(\alpha - \omega^2 + 3\beta a_1^2/4)^2 + 4\kappa^2\omega^2\}a_1^2 = f_1^2 , \qquad 39.3$$

which degenerates to 36.8 when $\kappa = 0$.

The amplitude-frequency curves now take the forms depicted
in Fig. 39.1A, B. Instead of two branches which never meet, to
each value of f_r there corresponds one curve in which the
branches are joined.

Jump effect. Starting at N in Fig. 39.1A, let the frequency of
the driving force be increased gradually. $|a_1|$ will follow curve
NPQ. At Q the tangent is vertical, $|a_1|$ jumps from Q to R
on the lower limb of the curve, and follows along RT thereafter.
If now ω is reduced gradually, the path will be TRS, a jump
from S to P, and then down towards N. The jumps indicate
instability. $|a_1|$ is single-valued to the left of PS and to the
right of QR, but between these two positions, it is triple-valued,
and in practice only one value can apply. Moreover, the part

---

*To avoid complication, loss associated with the third harmonic has
been neglected.

SQ lies in an unstable region, and *PQRS* is a form of hysteresis loop. The jump effect occurs also when $\beta < 0$, as will be evident on following similar procedure respecting Fig. 39.1B. The smaller the damping, the greater the interval between *PS* and *QR*, and the larger the loop. The curves for $\beta > 0$, $\beta < 0$, are similar to those for $\beta = 0$, $\kappa > 0$ in Fig. 23.1 sheared to the right and left, respectively. Experimental results will be found in reference [8a].

In a linear system $\beta = 0$ in 39.3, and when $\omega^2 = \alpha = \omega_1^2$, the mechanical reactance vanishes and resonance ensues. The term $(\alpha^2 - \omega^2 + 3\beta a_1^2/4)$ is never zero in the non-linear system, so resonance in the usually accepted sense does not occur.

40. SUBHARMONICS   When a system is driven by an alternating force of angular frequency ω, and the motion comprises one or more frequencies ω/n, $n = 2, 3, \cdots$, the latter are called subharmonics. If certain conditions are satisfied, subharmonics may occur in non-linear systems. Their existence up to $n = 10$, in systems having a characteristic of the form $f = \pm \{s_1 \mid x \mid + s_2 x^2 + s_3 \mid x^3 \mid + \cdots\}$, has been demonstrated experimentally [8b, 9]. We shall now demonstrate analytically that, when a certain condition is satisfied, a 1/3 harmonic* occurs in a loss-free system whose characteristic is Fig. 32.1A. The D.E. is, with $\beta > 0$,

$$\ddot{x} + \alpha x + \beta x^3 = f_1 \sin \omega t, \qquad 40.1$$

and we have to show that it has a periodic component solution $\sin \omega t/3$. As a first approximation assume that

$$x = a_{1/3} \sin \omega t/3 + a_1 \sin \omega t, \qquad 40.2$$

substitute into 40.1 and equate the coefficients of $\sin \omega t/3$ on each side. Then

$$a_{1/3}\{(\alpha - \omega^2/9) + (3\beta/4)(a_{1/3}^2 - a_{1/3}a_1 + 2a_1^2)\} = 0. \qquad 40.3$$

If there is a subharmonic, $a_{1/3} \neq 0$, so we must have

$$(\alpha - \omega^2/9) + (3\beta/4)(a_{1/3}^2 - a_{1/3}a_1 + 2a_1^2) = 0. \qquad 40.4$$

---

*A subharmonic of order 3.

Solving for $a_{1/3}$ yields

$$a_{1/3} = \{a_1 \pm [16(\omega^2 - 9\alpha)/27\beta - 7a_1^2]^{1/2}\}/2. \qquad 40.5$$

Since $a_{1/3}$ is real, it follows that

$$16(\omega^2 - 9\alpha)/27\beta - 7a_1^2 \geq 0, \qquad 40.6$$

or

$$\omega^2 \geq 9(\alpha + 21a_1^2\beta/16). \qquad 40.7$$

If f_1 has a suitable value, and ω is increased to

$$\omega = 3(\alpha + 21a_1^2\beta/16)^{1/2}, \qquad 40.8$$

the subharmonic starts, $|a_1|$ being on the lower limb of curve f_1 in Fig. 38.1C. Substituting from 40.8 into 40.5, the starting value is $a_{1/3} = -a_1/2$. Increase in ω is accompanied by that of $|a_{1/3}|$, which is ultimately much larger than $|a_1|$.

40.7 seems to be independent of f_1. This is only apparent, because 40.7 includes a_1, whose evaluation necessitates a second relationship obtained by equating the coefficients of sin ωt on both sides of 40.1 (after substituting 40.2). Details are given in reference [15].

For a certain ω, $a_1 = 0$ and the subharmonic exists alone. Substituting $x = a_{1/3} \sin \omega t/3$ into 40.1 and equating the coefficients of sin $\omega t/3$, sin ωt on both sides, we obtain $a_{1/3} = -\{4(\omega^2 - 9\alpha)/27\beta\}^{1/2} = -(4f_1/\beta)^{1/3}$. Thus for $a_1 = 0$, we must have $\omega^2 = 9\{\alpha + 3(f_1^2\beta/4)^{1/3}\}$. Since sin ωt = sin $(\omega t + 2n\pi)$, it follows that $a_{1/3}$ sin $(\omega t + 2\pi)/3$, $a_{1/3}$ sin $(\omega t + 4\pi)/3$ are also solutions. Accordingly there are three subharmonic solutions of equal amplitude which differ in phase by $2\pi/3$ radians. It may be shown that they are stable.*

★41. INTERMODULATION   If a force having several components of different frequencies acts on a *linear* system, the solution of the D.E. for the forced vibrations, is the sum of the individual solutions for the respective components. Thus each may be considered separately. *This cannot be done with a non-*

---

*[15, p. 188].

linear system, although for a single component the motion may be almost harmonic. Non-linearity of the characteristic causes one component to affect the other, and alien frequencies are created. To demonstrate the point analytically, we choose the D.E.

$$\ddot{x} + \omega_0^2 x + \beta x^3 = f_1 \sin \omega_1 t + f_2 \sin \omega_2 t, \qquad 41.1$$

where $\omega_0 \neq \omega_1 \neq \omega_2$, and assume absence of subharmonics. We shall use the method of iteration (successive approximation)* to solve 41.1. First we suppose $| \beta x^3 | \ll | \omega_0^2 x |$, and this leads to a consideration of the *linear* D.E.

$$\ddot{x} + \omega_0^2 x = f_1 \sin \omega_1 t + f_2 \sin \omega_2 t. \qquad 41.2$$

By 19.6 the solution for the forced oscillation is

$$x = \{ f_1/(\omega_0^2 - \omega_1^2) \} \sin \omega_1 t + \{ f_2/(\omega_0^2 - \omega_2^2) \} \sin \omega_2 t, \qquad 41.3$$

this being the first approximation, which has no non-linear features, since 41.2 is linear. Next we write 41.1 in the form

$$\ddot{x} + \omega_0^2 x = f_1 \sin \omega_1 t + f_2 \sin \omega_2 t - \beta x^3, \qquad 41.4$$

and substitute for x from 41.3 into the last term. Putting $g_1 = f_1 / (\omega_0^2 - \omega_1^2)$, $g_2 = f_2 / (\omega_0^2 - \omega_2^2)$, $\theta_1 = \omega_1 t$, $\theta_2 = \omega_2 t$, 41.4 becomes

$$\begin{aligned}
\ddot{x} + \omega_0^2 x = f_1 \sin \theta_1 + f_2 \sin \theta_2 - \{ G_1 \sin \theta_1 \\
+ G_2 \sin \theta_2 + G_3 \sin 3\theta_1 + G_4 \sin 3\theta_2 \\
+ G_s[\sin (2\theta_1 + \theta_2) - \sin (2\theta_1 - \theta_2)] \\
+ G_6[\sin (\theta_1 + 2\theta_2) + \sin (\theta_1 - 2\theta_2)] \},
\end{aligned} \qquad 41.5$$

where $\qquad G_1 = (3\beta/4)g_1^2(g_1 + g_2), \qquad G_2 = (3\beta/4)g_2(2g_1^2 + g_2^2),$

$$G_3 = -\beta g_1^3/4, \qquad\qquad G_4 = -\beta g_2^3/4,$$

*The procedure of successive approximation leads to the solution of linear D.E. We assume there is small damping, so the transient is negligible soon after application of the driving force, and initial conditions need not be introduced.

$$G_5 = -(3\beta/4)g_1^2 g_2 , \qquad G_6 = -(3\beta/4)g_1 g_2^2 .$$

The particular integral of 41.5 provides the required solution, which consists of each term on the r.h.s. multiplied by the proper factor. For instance the term in G_5 gives

$$\ddot{x} + \omega_0^2 x = -G_5\{\sin (2\theta_1 + \theta_2) - \sin (2\theta_1 - \theta_2)\}, \qquad 41.6$$

of which the p.i. is

$$x = -G_5\left\{\frac{\sin (2\theta_1 + \theta_2)}{\omega_0^2 - (2\omega_1 + \omega_2)^2} - \frac{\sin (2\theta_1 - \theta_2)}{\omega_0^2 - (2\omega_1 - \omega_2)^2}\right\}. \qquad 41.7$$

Hence in the expression for the displacement, i.e. the solution of 41.5, terms having the following frequencies occur: ω_1 , ω_2 the applied frequencies; $3\omega_1$, $3\omega_2$, third harmonics of ω_1 , ω_2 ; the sum frequencies $(2\omega_1 + \omega_2)$, $(\omega_1 + 2\omega_2)$,; and the difference frequencies $\mid 2\omega_1 - \omega_2 \mid$, $\mid \omega_1 - 2\omega_2 \mid$. Taking $\omega_1 = 2000$, $\omega_2 = 500$, the motion contains the angular frequencies 500, 1000, 1500, 2000, 3000, 3500, 4500, 6000. Starting with the two frequencies 500, 2000, the effect of the non-linear characteristic is to create the alien frequencies 1000, 1500, 3000, 4500, 6000. If the process of iteration were continued, additional frequencies would be revealed, in fact there is an infinity of them, but their amplitudes are relatively small.

In the numerical case above, the oscillation ω_1 moves over the curved characteristic four times as fast as ω_2 , so the first executes its individual oscillations at different parts thereof. The result is that intermodulation occurs.

An interesting example pertains to the human ear, whose characteristic is non-linear and asymmetrical. If two pure tones of adequate loudness are impressed upon the ear, four tones in particular are audible, namely, the originals, their sum and their difference. This case may be investigated by the reader using the D.E.

$$\ddot{x} + \alpha x + \beta x^2 = f_1 \sin \omega_1 t + f \sin \omega_2 t, \qquad 41.8$$

where in the first approximation, βx^2 may be neglected, and $\beta > 0$.

CHAPTER IV

Systems having More Than One Degree of Freedom

42. Two degrees of freedom   When two simple systems are interconnected, the combination may have two freedoms. For instance m_1 , s_1 and m_2 , s_2 are coupled by s, as shown in Fig. 42.1A. The motion of m_1 is described completely by x_1 , and that of m_2 by x_2 . Since two *independent* coordinates are

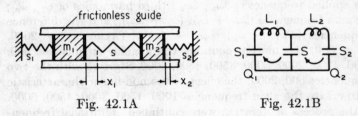

Fig. 42.1A   Fig. 42.1B

needed, the system is said to have two degrees of freedom. The composite system has two natural frequencies, but $\omega_1^2 \neq s_1/m_1$, $\omega_2^2 \neq s_2/m_2$, owing to modification caused by the coupling, for one mass cannot move without affecting the other.

Using the electrical analog in Fig. 42.1B, by Kirchhoff's law the sum of the p.d.s. in each mesh must vanish. For S_1L_1S

$$L_1\ddot{Q}_1 + S_1Q_1 + S(Q_1 - Q_2) = 0, \qquad 42.1$$

and for L_2S_2S

$$L_2\ddot{Q}_2 + S_2Q_2 - S(Q_1 - Q_2) = 0. \qquad 42.2$$

The analogous equations for the mechanical system are

$$m_1\ddot{x}_1 + s_1x_1 + s(x_1 - x_2) = 0, \qquad 42.3$$

and $$m_2\ddot{x}_2 + s_2x_2 - s(x_1 - x_2) = 0. \qquad 42.4$$

We shall solve these simultaneous linear D.E. for the initial conditions $x_1 = X$, $\dot{x}_1 = x_2 = \dot{x} = 0$ at $t = 0$, using operational calculus, based upon the Laplace transform where $x(t) \Rightarrow \phi(p)$. These initial conditions mean that m_1 is displaced by X, m_2 is held in its equilibrium position, and both m_1, m_2 are released at $t = 0$. For $x_1(t)$, $x_2(t)$ we write $\phi_1(p)$, $\phi_2(p)$, and p for d/dt, which yields the *transform* equations [13]

$$(p^2 + a_1^2)\phi_1 = b_1^2\phi_2 + Xp^2, \qquad 42.5$$

and
$$(p^2 + a_2^2)\phi_2 = b_2^2\phi_1, \qquad 42.6$$

where $a_1^2 = (s + s_1)/m_1$, $a_2^2 = (s + s_2)/m_2$, $b_1^2 = s/m_1$, $b_2^2 = s/m_2$, and the term Xp^2 arises from the initial condition $x_1 = X$.

Solving these as algebraic equations leads to

$$\phi_1 = Xp^2(p^2 + a_2^2)/\{(p^2 + a_1^2)(p^2 + a_2^2) - b_1^2 b_2^2\} \qquad 42.7$$

$$= Xp^2(p^2 + a_2^2)/(p^2 + \omega_1^2)(p^2 + \omega_2^2), \qquad 42.8$$

with
$$\omega_1^2, \omega_2^2 = (a_1^2 + a_2^2)\{1 \pm [1$$
$$42.9$$
$$- 4(a_1^2 a_2^2 - b_1^2 b_2^2)/(a_1^2 + a_2^2)^{1/2}\}/2,$$

both roots being real and positive, as the reader may verify. Resolving 42.8 into partial fractions gives

$$\phi_1 = \{X/(\omega_1^2 - \omega_2^2)\}\left\{\left(\frac{\omega_1^2 - a_2^2}{p^2 + \omega_1^2}\right)p^2 - \left(\frac{\omega_2^2 - a_2^2}{p^2 + \omega_2^2}\right)p^2\right\}. \qquad 42.10$$

Inverting 42.10 by aid of a list of L.T.S. yields

$$x_1(t) = \{X/(\omega_1^2 - \omega_2^2)\}\{(\omega_1^2 - a_2^2)\cos \omega_1 t$$
$$42.11$$
$$- (\omega_2^2 - a_2^2)\cos \omega_2 t\},$$

which satisfies the initial conditions $x_1 = X$, $\dot{x}_1 = 0$. Similarly, we obtain

$$x_2(t) = -\{Xb_2^2/(\omega_1^2 - \omega_2^2)\}(\cos \omega_1 t - \cos \omega_2 t), \qquad 42.12$$

which satisfies the initial conditions $x_2 = \dot{x}_2 = 0$.

42.11, 42.12 show that there are two frequencies (normal modes of vibration) ω_1, ω_2 given by 42.9, both of which differ from that for either system vibrating independently, i.e. when $s = 0$. In this latter case, 42.3, 42.4 yield $\omega_1^2 = s_1/m_1$, and $\omega_2^2 = s_2/m_2$. It appears, therefore, that s is an index of the

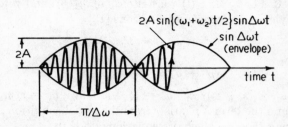

Fig. 43.1.

degree of coupling between the two systems. $(\omega_1 - \omega_2)$ increases with increase in s. One frequency is larger and the other smaller than that with $s = 0$.

43. BEATS   42.12 may be written

$$x_2(t) = A(\cos \omega_1 t - \cos \omega_2 t) \qquad 43.1$$

$$= 2A \sin \{(\omega_1 + \omega_2)t/2\} \sin \{(\omega_1 - \omega_2)t/2\}, \qquad 43.2$$

where A is the external multiplier. 43.2 shows that the first function is modulated by the second and vice-versa, i.e. there is a variation in amplitude with time. If ω_1/ω_2 is a proper fraction, the motion is periodic although the amplitude varies.

When the parameters of the system are such that $\omega_1 \simeq \omega_2$ we may write $\omega_2 = \omega_1 - 2\Delta\omega$, and 43.2 becomes

$$x_2(t) = 2A \sin \{(\omega_1 + \omega_2)t/2\} \sin (\Delta\omega)t. \qquad 43.3$$

The ratio of the period of $\sin (\Delta\omega)t$ to that of $\sin \{(\omega_1 + \omega_2)t/2\}$ is nearly $\omega_1/\Delta\omega \gg 1$. Thus x_2 may be regarded as an oscillation whose amplitude varies or is modulated at a relatively slow rate. When $t = n\pi/\Delta\omega$, $\sin (\Delta\omega)t = 0$, and the amplitude is zero, as illustrated in Fig. 43.1. This effect is known as 'beats', the terminology being derived from acoustics. For instance when two strings for the same note on a pianoforte are slightly out of tune, a listener hears the sound waxing and waning (beating). The beats disappear when the strings are in unison, and there is then only one frequency audible (apart from the harmonics of the strings). This principle is used extensively in audio and in radio frequency checking systems.

44. IMPULSE $SI(t)$ APPLIED TO m_1 IN FIG. 42.1A   Prior to $t = 0$, the system is quiescent, and the impulse is applied *at* $t = 0$. 42.4 and 42.6 are unchanged, but for 42.3, 42.5, we have, respectively,

$$m_1\ddot{x}_1 + s_1x_1 + s(x_1 - x_2) = SI(t), \qquad 44.1$$

and
$$(p^2 + a_1^2)\phi_1 = b_1^2\phi_2 + Sp/m_1 , \qquad 44.2$$

since $I(t) \Rightarrow p$. Then on comparison with 42.5, ϕ_1 is given by 42.10 if Xp^2 is replaced by Sp/m_1 . Hence

$$\phi_1 = \{(S/m_1)/(\omega_1^2 - \omega_2^2)\}\left\{\left(\frac{\omega_1^2 - a_2^2}{p^2 + \omega_1^2}\right)p - \left(\frac{\omega_2^2 - a_2^2}{p^2 + \omega_2^2}\right)p\right\}, \qquad 44.3$$

so
$$x_1(t) = \{(S/m_1)/(\omega_1^2 - \omega_2^2)\}\left\{\left(\frac{\omega_1^2 - a_2^2}{\omega_1}\right)\sin \omega_1 t\right.$$

$$44.5$$

$$\left. - \left(\frac{\omega_2^2 - a_2^2}{\omega_2}\right)\sin \omega_2 t\right\}.$$

This expression shows that the uniform band spectrum of $I(t)$ has been converted into a two line spectrum at $\omega = \omega_1 , \omega_2$.*

45. FORCED VIBRATION   Suppose that m_1 in Fig. 42.1A is driven by a force $f \cos \omega t$, then 42.3 must be replaced by

---

*We have tacitly assumed the system to be an 'idealised' type having only two natural vibrations. In a practical system, the infinite sets of vibrations of both masses and springs, considered as continuous systems, would be excited (see §1). A problem of this complexity is beyond our present purpose.

$$m_1\ddot{x}_1 + s_1 x_1 + s(x_1 - x_2) = f \cos \omega t, \qquad 45.1$$

but 42.4 is unchanged. Since $\cos \omega t \rightleftharpoons p^2/(p^2 + \omega^2)$, the transform equations for initial quiescence,† are

$$(p^2 + a_1^2)\phi_1 = b_1^2\phi_2 + f_1 p^2/(p^2 + \omega^2), \qquad 45.2$$

and $\qquad (p^2 + a_2^2)\phi_2 = b_2^2\phi_1 , \qquad 45.3$

where $f_1 = f/m_1$. Solving 45.2, 45.3, as simultaneous algebraic equations, we get

$$\phi_1 = f_1 p^2(p^2 + a_2^2)/(p^2 + \omega_1^2)(p^2 + \omega_2^2)(p^2 + \omega^2). \qquad 45.4$$

There are free and forced vibrations. To obtain the latter *independently*, we effect inversion of 45.4 by the Mellin theorem [12]. Thus

$$x_1(t) = \frac{f_1}{2\pi i} \int_{c-i\infty}^{c+i\infty} \frac{e^{zt}z(z^2 + a_2^2)\, dz}{(z^2 + \omega_1^2)(z^2 + \omega_2^2)(z^2 + \omega^2)} . \qquad (45.5)$$

The forced vibration of m_1 is got by summing the residues at the poles $z = \pm i\omega$.* The residue at $z = i\omega$ is

$$f_1 e^{i\omega t} i\omega(a_2^2 - \omega^2)/(\omega_1^2 - \omega^2)(\omega_2^2 - \omega^2)2i\omega, \qquad 45.6$$

while the residue at $z = -i\omega$, is 45.6 with $-i$ for i. Adding these gives the forced vibration of m_1 , namely,

$$x_1(t) = \{ f_1(a_2^2 - \omega^2)/(\omega_1^2 - \omega^2)(\omega_2^2 - \omega^2) \} \cos \omega t. \qquad 45.7$$

Similarly for m_2 ,

$$x_2(t) = b_2^2 x_1(t)/(a_2^2 - \omega^2). \qquad 45.8$$

We infer from 45.7, 45.8, that**m_1 , m_2 , move in the same direction if $\omega < a_2$, but in opposite directions if $\omega > a_2$. Also when $\omega \to a_2$, $x_1 \to 0$; m_1 tends to rest although m_2 is in motion.

———————

†Zero displacement and velocity.

*We assume that $\omega \neq \omega_1 , \omega_2 , a_2$.

**In the absence of free vibrations.

This effect, usually employed when $s_2 = 0$, is the basis of an anti-vibration device, ω being constant. In practice the motion is modified due to loss, and although the amplitude of m_1 is small, it cannot be zero. To cope with a disturbing force of of variable frequency, a damper is attached to m thereby making the system less selective [17].

46. MECHANICAL IMPEDANCE   Replacing cos ωt in 45.7 by $e^{i\omega t}$ and differentiating, yields

$$\dot{x}_1 = if\{\omega(a_2^2 - \omega^2)/(\omega_1^2 - \omega^2)(\omega_2^2 - \omega^2)m_1\}, \qquad 46.1$$

so the mechanical *input* impedance at m_1 is

$$z_1 = f/\dot{x}_1 = -i\{(\omega_1^2 - \omega^2)(\omega_2^2 - \omega^2)/\omega(a_2^2 - \omega^2)\}m_1 , \qquad 46.2$$

which $\to +\infty$ as $\omega \to a_2$, i.e. m_1 tends to rest as stated in §45. 46.2 is not valid *at* $\omega = \omega_1$, ω_2 , since double poles would occur in the integrand of 45.5, thereby entailing a factor t in the residues. Nevertheless 46.2 indicates that $z_1 \to 0$, as ω approaches either of the vibrational modes of the system.

The drive at m_1 is transferred via s to m_2 , and the *transfer* impedance is by 45.8, using the above procedure,

$$z_2 = f/\dot{x}_2 = (a_2^2 - \omega^2)z_1/b_2^2 . \qquad 46.3$$

From the symmetry of the arrangement in Fig. 42.1A, it is evident that if m_2 is driven instead of m_1 , all the above results are valid provided the subscripts 1, 2, are interchanged.

47. LAGRANGE'S EQUATIONS   Referring to Fig. 2.1A, the K.E. of m is $T = m\dot{x}^2/2$, so $\partial T/\partial\dot{x} = m\dot{x}$, and, therefore,

$$\frac{d}{dt}\left(\frac{\partial T}{\partial\dot{x}}\right) = m\ddot{x}. \qquad 47.1$$

The potential energy stored in the spring is $V = sx^2/2$, so

$$\partial V/\partial x = sx. \qquad 47.2$$

Hence 3.1 may be written in the Lagrangian form

$$\frac{d}{dt}\left(\partial T/\partial \dot{x}\right) + \partial V/\partial x = 0. \qquad 47.3$$

For the system of Fig. 42.1A, the sum of the K.E. of m_1, m_2, is

$$T = (m_1\dot{x}_1^2 + m_2\dot{x}_2^2)/2, \qquad 47.4$$

while the P.E. stored in the springs s, s_1, s_2, is

$$V = \{s_1x_1^2 + s(x_1 - x_2)^2 + s_2x_2^2\}/2. \qquad 47.5$$

Thus

$$\frac{d}{dt}(\partial T/\partial \dot{x}_1) = m_1\ddot{x}_1, \quad \text{and} \quad \partial V/\partial x_1 = s_1x_1 + s(x_1 - x_2), \qquad 47.6$$

so by aid of 47.3 we reproduce 42.3. Similarly by differentiating with regard to x_2, $\dot{x}_2$, 42.4 is obtained. The method of solution is that in §42.

48. EXAMPLE [22] We now apply Lagrange's equations to the system shown schematically in Fig. 48.1A where a rigid

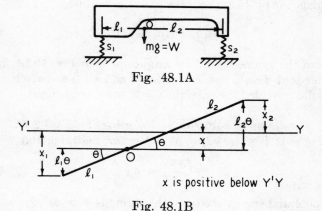

Fig. 48.1A

Fig. 48.1B

structure of mass m, centre of gravity O, is supported by two vertical springs of stiffnesses s_1, s_2. There are more than two degrees of freedom, but we shall consider only those arising from motion in a vertical plane, namely, (i) O moves in a vertical direction, (ii) the structure oscillates about O in a vertical plane. Then the motion is described completely by the two coordinates x, θ, so the system has two degrees of freedom.

If θ in Fig. 48.1B is small, and x is the distance of the c.g. from $Y'Y$, we have

$$x_1 = x + l_1\theta, \quad \text{and} \quad x_2 = x - l_2\theta. \qquad 48.1$$

Also if I is the moment of inertia of the structure about 0 (see 14.3)

$$T = (m\dot{x}^2 + I\dot{\theta}^2)/2, \qquad 48.2$$

and

$$V = (s_1 x_1^2 + s_2 x_2^2)/2$$

$$= \{s_1(x + l_1\theta)^2 + s_2(x - l_2\theta)^2\}/2. \qquad 48.3$$

Thus

$$\partial T/\partial \dot{x} = m\dot{x}, \quad \text{so} \quad \frac{d}{dt}(\partial T/\partial \dot{x}) = m\ddot{x}, \qquad 48.4$$

$$\partial V/\partial x = s_1(x + l_1\theta) + s_2(x - l_2\theta), \qquad 48.5$$

$$\frac{d}{dt}(\partial T/\partial \dot{\theta}) = I\ddot{\theta}, \qquad 48.6$$

and

$$\partial V/\partial \theta = l_1 s_1(x + l_1\theta) - l_2 s_2(x - l_2\theta). \qquad 48.7$$

By 47.3, 48.4, 48.5

$$m\ddot{x} + (s_1 + s_2)x + (l_1 s_1 - l_2 s_2)\theta = 0, \qquad 48.8$$

or

$$\ddot{x} + a_1^2 x + b_1^2 \theta = 0, \qquad 48.9$$

with

$$a_1^2 = (s_1 + s_2)/m, \quad b_1^2 = (l_1 s_1 - l_2 s_2)/m.$$

Similarly from 48.6, 48.7

$$\ddot{\theta} + a_2^2 \theta + b_2^2 x = 0, \qquad 48.10$$

with $\qquad a_2^2 = (l_1^2 s_1 + l_2^2 s_2)/\mathbf{I}, \qquad b_2^2 = (l_1 s_1 - l_2 s_2)/\mathbf{I}.$

If $l_1 s_1 = l_2 s_2$, the statical compressions of the springs are equal, $b = 0$, so 48.9 is independent of θ, and 48.10 of x. Hence there is no coupling and the two vibrations of frequencies a_1, a_2, occur *independently*. Moreover mb_1^2 is an index of the degree of coupling between the two freedoms. Now $l_1 s_1 - l_2 s_2 = ls_1 - l_2(s_1 + s_2)$ and this has its largest positive value when $l_2 = 0$. Thus the fractional coupling may be defined as

$$\{ls_1 - l_2(s_1 + s_2)\}/ls_1 = 1 - l_2(s_1 + s_2)/ls_1. \qquad 48.11$$

If we take $x = X$,* $\dot{x} = \theta = \dot{\theta} = 0$, at $t = 0$, the transform equations corresponding to 48.9, 48.10 are

$$(p^2 + a_1^2)\phi_1 = -b_1^2 \phi_2 + Xp^2, \qquad 48.12$$

and $\qquad (p^2 + a_2^2)\phi_2 = -b_2^2 \phi_1, \qquad 48.13$

being identical in form with 42.5, 42.6. Hence altering the symbols accordingly, the solutions of 48.9, 48.10 for the foregoing initial conditions are given by 42.11, 42.12.

49. n DEGREES OF FREEDOM   A system is said to have n degrees of freedom if n *independent* coordinates are required to describe its motion completely. The free motion of a rigid structure may be completely described by six coordinates; x, y, z, for linear translation and θ, χ, ψ for angular rotation. If the motion of the whole system occurs in one plane, the procedure set out in §§42-48 may be employed to derive the set of n *ordinary* D.E. of the second order. In the general case, all parts of the system do not move in the same plane, and it is then necessary to derive Lagrange's equations in terms of generalised coordinates and generalised forces. This is beyond our

---

*The statical displacement due to mg has been ignored since it entails merely a change of origin. X is the additional vertical displacement of O at $t = 0$ (see §6).

present purview, and the reader is referred to [5, 22]. Usually the D.E. may be solved most readily by operational calculus, which permits inclusion of the driving forces and the initial conditions prior to solution of the transform equation, as has been demonstrated in §§42-48.

CHAPTER V

Vibration of Flexible Strings

50. A CONTINUOUS SYSTEM was defined in §1. Since the motion, in general, differs throughout the system, if it were described point by point using independent coordinates, an infinite number of them would be required. The shape at any instant is given by $f(x)$, say, a function of x. Mathematically an infinite number of values is needed to determine the configuration completely, so there would be an unlimited number of coordinates. Thus there is an infinite number of degrees of freedom. The shape may also be represented by a Fourier series, which in turn has an infinite number of coefficients.

In dealing with continuous systems, it is expedient to make the following assumptions to simplify the analysis: (a) vibration occurs *in vacuo*; (b) there is absence of loss; (c) the system is elastic and its force-displacement characteristic linear; (d) the maximum displacement (amplitude) is small; (e) deformation due to gravity may be neglected. As regards (a), the 'accession to inertia' of a circular membrane of aluminium foil 0.2 metre radius may reduce the frequency of the fundamental symmetrical mode (in air) by more than 50 per cent. The dynamic deformation surface is altered in shape also. Concerning (b), a small loss ultimately extinguishes a 'free' vibration, but has little influence on its rate. In practice, however, loss increases rapidly with rise in frequency, so only the fundamental and a few early overtones are obtained to any extent. The higher overtones are damped so much that they occur as non-oscillatory decay transients of negligible maxima. The restriction (d) is to ensure constant conditions. For instance in Fig. 51.1, $T_2 = (T^2 + T_1^2)^{1/2} \simeq T\{1 + (T_1/T)^2/2\}$ provided $T_1 \ll T$, so if ξ is small, $T_2 \simeq T$, which may be considered constant. The effect of variable tension of a string due to large amplitude is considered in [2]. The analysis herein is concerned with 'ideal' strings having flexibility but not stiffness. The tension provides the restoring force, just as inherent stiffness does in the case of a bar or a spring.

Since any linear continuous system subject to hypotheses (a)-(e) has an infinity of vibrational modes, a linear *partial* D.E. is needed to describe the motion, because it yields an infinite set of solutions. Such equations are usually of the second or fourth order in x, but of the second order in t, in virtue of a term of the type $m\ddot{x}$. The number of boundary (initial) conditions is equal to the order of the D.E. with respect to displacement (time).

51. TRANSVERSE FREE VIBRATION OF UNIFORM STRING HELD AT EACH END   Referring to Fig. 51.1, by similar triangles

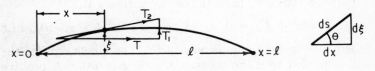

Fig. 51.1

$$\partial\xi/\partial x = T_1/T, \quad \text{so} \quad T_1 = T\partial\xi/\partial x, \qquad 51.1$$

and
$$\partial T_1/\partial x = \frac{\partial}{\partial x}(T\partial\xi/\partial x) = T\partial^2\xi/\partial x^2, \qquad 51.2$$

since, by hypothesis, T is constant. The net force acting on an element of length $ds \simeq dx$, is the difference between the values of T_1 at each end, and by 51.2 this is

$$\partial T_1 = T(\partial^2\xi/\partial x^2)\, dx. \qquad 51.3$$

The force to accelerate the element is its mass $\times$ acceleration, so

$$\partial T_1 = (\mathbf{m}\, dx)\partial^2\xi/\partial t^2, \qquad 51.4$$

$\mathbf{m}$ being the mass per unit length. Equating 51.3, 51.4, yields the linear *partial* D.E.

$$\partial^2\xi/\partial t^2 = c^2\partial^2\xi/\partial x^2, \qquad 51.5$$

where $c = (T/\mathbf{m})^{1/2}$, having the units of velocity, lt^{-1}.

Now a partial D.E. may have more than one form of solution, so we must choose that which is suitable for the present problem. From experience this is known to be the product type

$$\xi(x, t) = f(x)g(t), \qquad 51.6$$

where $f(x)$ is a function of x alone, and $g(t)$ is a function of t alone. Substituting 51.6 into 51.5, and dividing throughout by fg, yields

$$(1/g)(d^2g/dt^2) = (c^2/f)(d^2f/dt^2). \qquad 51.7$$

The l.h.s. is independent of x, and the r.h.s. of t, and since they have to be equal for $t > 0$, $0 \leq x \leq l$, it follows that each must be a constant. Taking this to be $-\omega^2$ (known as the separation constant) leads to the two *ordinary* D.E.

$$d^2f/dx^2 + k^2f = 0, \qquad \text{and} \qquad d^2g/dt^2 + \omega^2g = 0, \quad 51.8$$

where $k = \omega/c$, having dimension l^{-1}. The minus sign for the s.c. is needed to make the equation in t *periodic*. A positive sign would entail hyperbolic functions which $\rightarrow +\infty$ with t.

The respective solutions of the D.E. in 51.8 are:

$$f(x) = A \sin kx + B \cos kx, \quad g(t) = C \sin \omega t + D \cos \omega t, \quad 51.9$$

where A-D are arbitrary constants. The boundary conditions are (i) $\xi = 0$, $x = 0$, (ii) $\xi = 0$, $x = l$, so the solution cannot contain $\cos kx$. Thus the required form is

$$\xi(x, t) = f(x)g(t) = \sin kx \,(C \cos \omega t + D \sin \omega t), \quad 51.10$$

the arbitrary constant A being absorbed into C, D. To satisfy the second b.c., we must have

$$\sin kl = 0, \qquad 51.11$$

since neither C nor D need be zero. Thus $kl = n\pi$, $n = 1, 2, \cdots$. 51.11 is called the frequency equation, for it gives

$$kl = n\pi, \qquad \text{or} \qquad \omega_n = n\pi c/l = n(\pi/l)(T/\mathbf{m})^{1/2}. \qquad 51.12$$

Each n corresponds to a different mode of vibration. When $n = 1$, the string vibrates in the same phase throughout its length; when $n = 2$, $\xi(l/2, t) = 0$, and a node* occurs at $x = l/2$, on each side of which the string moves in opposite phase, and so on. In $x = (0, l)$, $\sin k_n x = \sin (n\pi x/l)$ vanishes $(n - 1)$ times, so there are $(n - 1)$ nodes *between* the supports. The configurations for several n are shown in Fig. 51.2. By 51.12 the periodic time is $2l/nc$, which is the interval of travel between a node and the next node but one. When $n = 1$, $2l/c$ is the time taken to travel from one support to the other and back again (due to reflection).

Inserting ω_n for ω and $k_n = n\pi/l$ for k in 51.10, gives the solution of 51.5 for the nth mode, and since $n = 1, 2, \cdots$, it follows that the general solution, i.e. the sum of all the particular solutions, is

$$\xi(x, t) = \sum_{n=1}^{\infty} \sin (n\pi x/l)\{C_n \sin \omega_n t + D_n \cos \omega_n t\}. \qquad 51.13$$

This exemplifies the remarks on degrees of freedom in §50. Moreover, in *general* when a string is vibrating after being impulsed, there is a fundamental and as infinite number of *harmonic* overtones whose frequency ratios follow the sequence of the positive integers, i.e. $\omega_n = n\omega_1$.

52. DETERMINATION OF C, D, IN 51.13 Let $t = 0$ and we have

$$\xi(x, 0) = \sum_{m=1}^{\infty} D_m \sin (m\pi x/l),$$

$$52.1$$

$$\xi(x, 0) = \sum_{m=1}^{\infty} \omega_m C_m \sin (m\pi x/l).$$

Multiplying both sides of these expressions by $\sin (n\pi x/l)\ dx$ and integrating from $x = (0, l)$, in virtue of orthogonality, all

---

*In practice, owing to loss, a true node cannot occur in any vibrating system. It is merely a position of least amplitude.

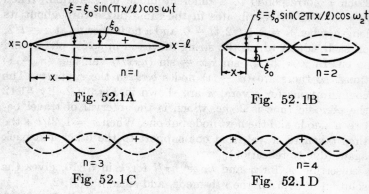

Fig. 52.1A

Fig. 52.1B

n=3
Fig. 52.1C

n=4
Fig. 52.1D

integrals vanish save when $m = n$, so

$$D_n = (2/l) \int_0^l \xi(x, 0) \sin (n\pi x/l) \, dx, \qquad 52.2$$

and

$$C_n = (2/\omega_n l) \int_0^l \dot{\xi}(x, 0) \sin (n\pi x/l) \, dx. \qquad 52.3$$

Thus when the displacement and velocity at $t = 0$ are specified, 52.2, 52.3 permit the subsequent values of these quantities to be calculated from 51.13.

53. PLUCKED STRING The shape before release is depicted in Fig. 53.1, and the initial conditions are:

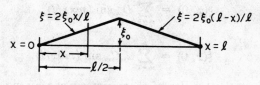

Fig. 53.1

(i) $\xi(x, 0) = 2\xi_0 x/l$, $0 \leq x \leq l/2$; $\xi(x, 0) = 2\xi_0(l - x)/l$, $l/2 \leq x \leq l$:

(ii) $\xi(x, 0) = 0, 0 \leq x \leq l$.

Inserting (i) into 52.2, we obtain

$$D_n = (4\xi_0/l^2)\left\{\int_0^{l/2} x \sin (n\pi x/l)\, dx\right.$$

$$\left. + \int_{l/2}^l (l - x) \sin (n\pi x/l)\, dx\right\}, \qquad 53.1$$

$$= (8\xi_0/\pi^2 n^2) \sin n\pi/2. \qquad 53.2$$

Now $\sin p\pi/2 = 0$ when $p = 2n$, but has the value $(-1)^{n-1}$ if $p = 2n - 1$, so

$$D_n = (-1)^{n-1} 8\xi_0/\pi^2 (2n - 1)^2. \qquad 53.3$$

By (ii) and 52.3, $C_n = 0$. Substituting this and D_n from 53.3 into 51.13, yields

$$\xi(x, t) = (8\xi_0/\pi^2) \sum_{n=1}^{\infty} (-1)^{n-1}\{1/(2n - 1)^2\}$$

$$\cdot \sin \{(2n - 1)\pi x/l\}\, \cos \omega_{2n-1} t. \qquad 53.4$$

The factor $1/(2n - 1)^2$ ensures absolute and uniform convergence of this series in $0 \leq x \leq l$. If $\cos \omega_{2n-1} t$ is omitted, the remainder is the Fourier expansion for Fig. 53.1.

53.4 shows that only *odd* harmonics accompany the fundamental vibration, their relative amplitudes being $1/9$, $1/25$, $\cdots$. The centre of the string is nodal for *all even* harmonics, and since it is plucked there, these harmonics are absent. In general all harmonics having a node at the plucked point are absent. This applies also to a struck string, and in a pianoforte the striking point is usually such that certain unwanted harmonics are suppressed.

54. GENERAL SOLUTION OF 51.5 The form at 51.6 is *not* the general solution. This is given by

$$\xi(x, t) = f_1(x - ct) + f_2(x + ct), \qquad 54.1$$

where f_1 and f_2 are *arbitrary* functions of x, t. Moreover, the number of different solutions is unlimited. If 54.1 is inserted into 51.5, the D.E. is satisfied. x and ct have dimension l, so c is the velocity of propagation of a disturbance *of any form*

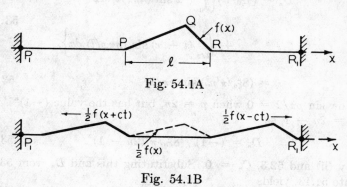

Fig. 54.1A

Fig. 54.1B

along the string, i.e. it is independent of frequency. When $t = 0$, the first solution is $f_1(x)$, and as t increases, $ct = x_1$ may be regarded as moving the origin to the variable point $+x_1$. Thus the disturbance $f_1(x)$ travels along the string towards the right. Similarly $f_2(x)$ travels towards the left. Since 54.1 is the general solution, it follows from what precedes that motion of the string may be regarded as the sum of two waves travelling in opposite directions with velocity c.

If $\xi(x, 0) = f(x)$, $\xi(x, 0) = 0$, the string starts from rest and the solution is then

$$\xi(x, t) = \{f(x - ct) + f(x + ct)\}/2, \qquad 54.2$$

so the two waves travelling in opposite directions are identical in shape. Let the initial configuration be P_1PQRR_1 (Fig. 54.1A), so that $f(x)$ is PQR. Then each wave is represented at $t = 0$ by the broken line in Fig. 54.1B. On releasing the string, the waves start to move in opposite directions, and after a time interval l/c, the configuration is that of the solid line in Fig. 54.1B. On arrival at the supports P_1 , R_1 , reflection occurs and the waves have their directions and phases reversed. Reflection occurs again on next reaching the supports, so the waves keep on travelling backwards and forwards between them. The shape of the string at any instant is the resultant of the multiple reflections, and this is expressible in a Fourier series, each of whose terms represents a natural vibration corresponding to a length P_1R_1. When P_1, R_1, respectively, and P, R, are coincident, a case of the type in §53 is obtained.

For a second example, let $f(x) = \xi_0 \sin (2\pi x/l)$, as in Fig. 52.1B. Then by 54.2

$$\xi(x, t) = (\xi_0/2)\{\sin [2\pi(x - ct)/l] + \sin [2\pi(x + ct)/l]\} \qquad 54.3$$

$$= \xi_0 \sin (2\pi x/l) \cos (2\pi ct/l), \qquad 54.4$$

which satisfies the boundary conditions $\xi(x, t) = 0$, at $x = 0$, l. Hence, after being released, the string preserves its original shape and vibrates in the second mode with $\omega_2 = 2\pi c/l$ (see Fig. 52.1B).

55. **UNIFORM STRING DRIVEN TRANSVERSELY AT ONE END** It is fixed at $x = 0$ and driven by a force $f \cos \omega t$ at $x = l$. Re-

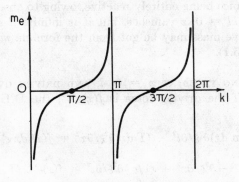

Fig. 55.1

ferring to 51.1 and Fig. 51.1, the force at $x = l$ must be equal to $T(\partial \xi/\partial x)$, and we shall consider upward displacement to be positive. Using 51.10,

$$f \cos \omega t = T(\partial \xi / \partial x)_{x=l} = Tk \cos kl \, (C \sin \omega t + D \cos \omega t), \quad 55.1$$

so $C = 0$, and $D = f/Tk \cos kl$. Substituting into the r.h.s. of 51.10 for C, D, yields

$$\xi(x, t) = \{f/\omega(\mathbf{m}T)^{1/2}\} \, (\sin kx/ \cos kl) \cos \omega t, \quad 55.2$$

and the velocity is

$$\dot\xi(x, t) = -\{f/(\mathbf{m}T)^{1/2}\} \, (\sin kx/ \cos kl) \sin \omega t. \quad 55.3$$

When $\cos kl = 0$, $k_n l = (2n - 1)\pi/2$, $n = 1, 2, \cdots$, and ξ is infinite (in theory!) except at $x = 0$. This corresponds to the natural vibrations of the string. When $\sin kl = 0$, $k_n l = n\pi$, ξ is zero at $x = l$, and also at intermediate points where $kx = \pi, 2\pi, \cdots (n - 1)\pi \cdots$, these being nodes.

Input or driving point impedance. Replacing $\cos \omega t$ by $e^{i\omega t}$ in 55.2,

$$\dot\xi(l, t) = (ife^{i\omega t} \tan kl)/(\mathbf{m}T)^{1/2}, \quad 55.4$$

so $$z = fe^{i\omega t}/\dot\xi(l, t) = -i(\mathbf{m}T)^{1/2} \cot kl, \quad 55.5$$

the impedance being entirely reactive, owing to absence of loss. When $\cos kl = 0$, z vanishes, but it is infinite if $\sin kl = 0$. The effective mass may be got from the formula $m_e = -iz/\omega$ (see Fig. 55.1).

56. String fixed at $x = 0$, l, and driven over entire length If the driving force is $f(x)e^{i\omega t}$, the D.E. takes the form

$$(\mathbf{m} \, dx)\partial^2\xi/\partial t^2 - (T \, dx)\partial^2\xi/\partial x^2 = f(x) \, dx \, e^{i\omega t}, \quad 56.1$$

so $$-\partial^2\xi/\partial x^2 + (1/c^2)\partial^2\xi/\partial t^2 = f(x)e^{i\omega t}/T. \quad 56.2$$

For the forced vibration we put $\xi(x, t) = \xi_1(x)e^{i\omega t}$, and 56.2 gives

$$d^2\xi_1/dx^2 + k^2\xi_1 = -f(x)/T. \quad 56.3$$

If the driving force is uniformly distributed over the string,

$f(x) = f_0$, a constant, this being the force per unit length, so

$$d^2\xi_1/dx^2 + k^2\xi_1 = -f_0/T, \qquad 56.4$$

of which the complete solution is

$$\xi_1(x) = A \sin kx + B \cos kx - f_0/k^2T. \qquad 56.5$$

The boundary conditions are $\xi_1 = 0$, at $x = 0, l$. Substituting into 56.5, we obtain

$$\xi_1(x) = (f_0/k^2T)\{(\cos kx - 1)$$

$$+ [(1 - \cos kl)/\sin kl] \sin kx\}, \quad 56.6$$

and after reduction

$$\xi(x, t) = (f_0/\omega^2\mathbf{m})\{[\cos k(x - l/2)/\cos kl/2] - 1\}e^{i\omega t}. \qquad 56.7$$

The mechanical impedance per unit length at x, is

$$\mathbf{z} = f_0/\xi = -if_0/\omega\xi$$

$$= -i\omega\mathbf{m}/\{[\cos k(x - l/2)/\cos kl/2] - 1\}, \qquad 56.8$$

and the effective mass is $\mathbf{m}_e = -i\mathbf{z}/\omega$, per unit length of string. When $kl = (2n - 1)\pi$, $0 < x < l$, $\mathbf{z}$ is infinite as also is $\mathbf{m}_e$. These infinities correspond to the odd natural vibrations of the string.

★57. STRING DRIVEN TRANSVERSELY AT INTERMEDIATE POINT In §56 the *total* uniformly distributed force on the string is $f = f_0 l$. Imagine this to be distributed over a short length Δx at $x = h$, such that $f_0\Delta x = f$ is constant (see §29). Then as $\Delta x \to 0$,* $f_0 \to + \infty$, and we get the analytical equivalent of an impulse $fI(x - h)$. In the notation of operational calculus, $fI(x - h) \rightleftharpoons fqe^{-qh}$ (where $x \rightleftharpoons 1/q$), and this may be used in the transform equation for 56.3 to designate the force f applied at the point $x = h$. It should be noticed that the L.T. refers

---

*In practice Δx cannot vanish, because the length of the driving clamp must be finite. But if Δx is small enough, the analysis given here provides an adequate answer to the problem.

to x and not t, so the 'boundary' conditions replace the 'initial' conditions. Taking $\xi_1(x) \Rightarrow \psi(q)$ in 56.3, the transform equation is [13],

$$(q^2 + k^2)\psi = -(f/T)qe^{-qh} + q^2\xi_1(0) + q\xi_1'(0). \qquad 57.1$$

The last two terms are associated with the boundary conditions, namely, the displacement and slope at $x = 0$, of which only the former is known. Since $\xi_1(0) = 0$,

$$\psi = -(f/T)qe^{-qh}/(q^2 + k^2) + q\xi_1'(0)/(q^2 + k^2). \qquad 57.2$$

The inverse transform of 57.2 is

$$\xi_1(x) = -(f/kT)\sin k(x - h) + \{\xi_1'(0)/k\}\sin kx, \qquad 57.3$$

for the range $h \leq x \leq l$.

We have now to determine $\xi_1'(0)$ to satisfy the condition $\xi_1(l) = 0$. Then

$$-(f/kT)\sin k(l - h) + \{\xi_1'(0)/k\}\sin kl = 0, \qquad 57.4$$

so $\qquad\qquad \xi_1'(0) = (f/T)\sin k(l - h)/\sin kl. \qquad 57.5$

Substituting from 57.5 into 57.3, yields

$$\xi(x, t) = \xi_1(x)e^{i\omega t} = -(f/kT)\{\sin k(x - h)$$

$$- \sin k(l - h)\sin kx/\sin kl\}e^{i\omega t}, \qquad 57.6$$

and after reduction

$$\xi(x, t) = \{f/\omega(\mathbf{m}T)^{1/2}\}\{\sin kh \sin k(l - x)/\sin kl\}e^{i\omega t}, \qquad 57.7$$

which applies in $h \leq x \leq l$.

To determine ξ in the range $0 \leq x \leq h$, we write x for $(l - x)$ and $(l - h)$ for h, i.e. interchange x and h, this procedure being valid since the known b.c. at each end of the string are identical.* Thus in $0 \leq x \leq h$,

$$\xi(x, t) = \{f/\omega(\mathbf{m}T)^{1/2}\}\{\sin k(l - h)\sin kx/\sin kl\}e^{i\omega t}. \qquad 57.8$$

---

*This refers to $\xi(0, t) = \xi(l, t) = 0$, but not to $\xi'(0, t)$, $\xi'(l, t)$ which are unknown initially.

57.7 has infinities corresponding to sin $kl = 0$, i.e. $kl = n\pi$, unless $kh = \pi, 2\pi, \cdots (n-1)\pi$. Then $\xi = 0$, because the driving force is applied at a point which would be nodal on a *freely* vibrating string. Similar deductions may be made from 57.8.

★58. SOLUTION FOR FORCED AND FREE VIBRATIONS In §56, at the outset we assumed harmonic motion, thereby obtaining 56.3. By so doing we failed to get the natural vibrations of the string, which occur whenever a force is applied suddenly (at $t = 0$). To determine these, we shall modify the method of solution.

The general D.E. is 56.2, but with $f(x)g(t)$† in place of $f(x)e^{i\omega t}$, where $f(x)$ and $g(t)$ are any suitable functions of x and t, respectively, which have Laplace transforms. Then

$$\partial^2\xi/\partial x^2 - (1/c^2)\partial^2\xi/\partial t^2 = -bf(x)g(t), \qquad 58.1$$

with $b = 1/T$. Taking $\xi(x, t) \Rightarrow \phi(x, p), g(t) \Rightarrow \phi_1(p)$ and writing p for $\partial/\partial t$, the transform equation for initial quiescence,* is

$$d^2\phi/dx^2 - \lambda^2\phi = -bf(x)\phi_1(p), \qquad 58.2$$

where $\lambda = p/c$.

We now solve this as an ordinary D.E. with independent variable x, using L.T. Accordingly we write q for d/dx and take $\phi(x, p) \Rightarrow \psi(q, p), f(x) \Rightarrow \psi_1(q)$. Then the transform equation is

$$(q^2 - \lambda^2)\psi = -b\psi_1(q)\phi_1(p) + q^2\phi(0) + q\phi'(0), \qquad 58.3$$

where the last two terms are associated with the conditions at $x = 0$.** Only one condition is known, namely, $\xi(0, t) = 0$, and since

---

†A product function of this type entails a function of t independent of x, and *vice-versa*.

*Initial quiescence means zero displacement and velocity at $t = 0$. If $\xi(x, 0), \dot{\xi}(x, 0)$ are not zero, $p^2\xi(x, 0) + p\dot{\xi}(x, 0)$ must be added to the r.h.s. of 58.2, these being the initial conditions terms [13].

**These correspond to the initial conditions when t is the independent variable.

$$\phi(x, p) = p \int_0^\infty e^{-pt} \xi(x, t) \, dt, \qquad 58.4$$

it follows that $\phi(0, p) = 0$. $\phi'(0)$ is unknown, but will be found later. Thus 58.3 reduces to

$$\psi = -b\psi_1\phi_1/(q^2 - \lambda^2) + \phi'(0)q/(q^2 - \lambda^2). \qquad 58.5$$

If the string is driven as in §57, $\psi_1 = fqe^{-qh}$. Inserting this into 58.5, yields

$$\psi = -bf\phi_1qe^{-qh}/(q^2 - \lambda^2) + \phi'(0)q/(q^2 - \lambda^2), \qquad 58.6$$

and by inversion

$$\phi = -(bf\phi_1/\lambda) \sinh \lambda(x - h) + \{\phi'(0)/\lambda\} \sinh \lambda x. \qquad 58.7$$

At $x = l$, $\xi(x, t) = 0$, so $\phi(l, p) = 0$, and by 58.7

$$\phi'(0) = bf\phi_1 \sinh \lambda(l - h)/\sinh \lambda l. \qquad 58.8$$

Inserting this into 58.7, gives

$$\phi(x, p) = (bf\phi_1/\lambda) \sinh \lambda(l - x) \sinh \lambda h/\sinh \lambda l, \qquad 58.9$$

which is the solution of 58.2 for the interval $h \leq x \leq l$.

To find $\xi(x, t) \Rightarrow \phi(x, p)$, we invert 58.9 by the Mellin theorem [12]. Taking $g(t) = \cos \omega t$, then $\phi_1(p) = p^2/(p^2 + \omega^2)$, so with $\lambda = z/c$,

$\xi(x, t)$

$$= (bcf/2\pi i) \int_{c-i\infty}^{c+i\infty} e^{zt} \left\{ \frac{\sinh [z(l - x)/c] \sinh (zh/c)}{(z^2 + \omega^2) \sinh (zl/c)} \right\} dz. \qquad 58.10$$

If ω is *not* a natural vibration of the string,* the singularities of the integrand of 58.10 are all *simple* poles, and the value of the integral is the sum of the residues thereat.† First we de-

---

*If $\omega = nc\pi/1$, $z = \pm inc\pi/1$ are zeros of both $(z^2 + \omega^2)$ and sinh zl/c, so double poles occur, the residues at which need special evaluation.

†As $z \to \infty$ there is a limit point for the poles. This feature is considered below 66.5.

termine the forced vibration by summing the residues at the poles $z = \pm i\omega$. Then for $z = i\omega$, with $k = \omega/c$,

$$\text{Residue} = (ie^{i\omega t}/2i\omega)\{\sin k(l - x) \sin kh/\sin kl\}. \qquad 58.11$$

For $z = -i\omega$, change i to $-i$, and the

$$\text{Residue} = (e^{-i\omega t}/2\omega)\{\text{as at } 58.11\}. \qquad 58.12$$

Adding 58.11, 58.12, and using the external multiplier from 58.10, yields

$$(f/kT)\{\sin k(l - x) \sin kh/\sin kl\}\cos \omega t, \qquad 58.13$$

which agrees with 57.7 in the range $h \leq x \leq l$, if the real part of $e^{i\omega t}$ is taken.

To obtain the natural vibrations, we sum the residues at the poles of integrand in 58.10, which arise from the zeros of sinh zl/c, except $z = 0$, which is not a pole. The zeros occur when $izl/c = n\pi$, or $z/c = -in\pi/l$, $\pm n = 1, 2, 3, \cdots$. Then

$\sum$ residues

$$= \sum_{n=1}^{\infty} \left\{\frac{e^{zt} \sinh [z(l - x)/c] \sinh (zh/c)}{(z^2 + \omega^2)d\{\sinh (xl/c)\}/dz}\right\}_{z/c = \pm in\pi/l} \qquad 58.14$$

$$= (c/l) \sum_{n=1}^{\infty} \left\{\frac{e^{zt} \sinh [z(l - x)/c] \sinh (zh/c)}{(z^2 + \omega^2) \cosh (zl/c)}\right\}_{z/c = \pm in\pi/l} \qquad 58.15$$

$$= (2c/l) \sum_{n=1}^{\infty} \sin (n\pi x/l) \sin (n\pi h/l) \cos (n\pi ct/l)/(\omega^2 - \omega_n^2), \quad 58.16$$

where $\omega_n = nc\pi/l$. Multiplying by bcf from 58.10, the displacement arising from the natural vibrations is

$$(2f/m) \sum_{n=1}^{\infty} (\text{as in } 58.16), \qquad 58.17$$

m being the mass of the whole string. 58.17 is valid when ω is *near* $nc\pi/l$, and then the denominator approaches zero, so the displacement corresponding to this frequency will be relatively large.

Finally, the displacement due to the forced and the free vibrations is the sum of 58.13 and 58.17, so in $h \leq x \leq l$,

$$\xi(x, t) = \{f/\omega(\mathbf{m}T)^{1/2}\}$$

$$\cdot \{\sin kh \sin k(l - x)/\sin kl\}\cos \omega t + 58.17. \qquad 58.18$$

For the interval $0 \leq x \leq h$, as in §57 we interchange x and h in 58.18.

Since the string started from rest, $\xi(x, 0)$ must vanish for all x at $t = 0$. Now the series in 58.16 is *uniformly* convergent in $0 \leq t_1 \leq t$, so we may put $t = 0$. Hence by 58.18 in $h \leq x \leq l$,

$$\{f/\omega(\mathbf{m}T)^{1/2}\}\left\{\frac{\sin kh \sin k(l - x)}{\sin kl}\right\}$$

$$= (2f/m) \sum_{n=1}^{\infty} \frac{\sin (n\pi x/l) \sin (n\pi h/l)}{(\omega_n^2 - \omega^2)}, \qquad 58.19$$

and in $0 \leq x \leq h$, by interchanging x and h in 58.19, we get

$$\{f/\omega(\mathbf{m}T)^{1/2}\}\left\{\frac{\sin k(l - h) \sin kx}{\sin kl}\right\} = \text{the r.h.s. of 58.19.} \qquad 58.20$$

By this simple artifice we have obtained the Fourier expansion of the expression for the amplitude of the forced vibration at any x.

59. STRING DRIVEN LONGITUDINALLY Here the driving agent of frequency $2\omega_0$ causes the end $x = l$ to move *along* the string, thereby varying its tension. If T is replaced by $T(1 - 2\gamma \cos 2\omega_0 t)$, the tension varies between the extreme limits $T(1 \pm 2\gamma)$, where we take $0 < \gamma < 0.5$. Then 51.5 becomes

$$\partial^2 \xi/\partial t^2 = (T/\mathbf{m})(1 - 2\gamma \cos 2\omega_0 t)\partial^2 \xi/\partial x^2. \qquad 59.1$$

Proceeding as in §51, we obtain the two ordinary D.E.,

$$d^2f/dx^2 + k^2 f = 0, \text{ and } d^2g/dt^2 + \omega^2(1 - 2\gamma \cos 2\omega_0 t)g = 0. \quad 59.2$$

The boundary conditions are $\xi = 0$ at $x = 0, l$, since the string does *not move transversely* at the driven end. Thus the solution

of the first equation in 59.2 has the form sin kx as in §51, and
there is an infinity of possible modes. We shall consider only

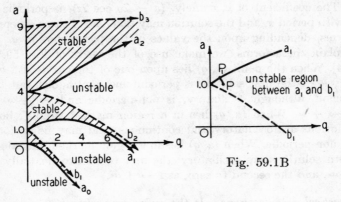

Fig. 59.1A

Fig. 59.1B

the fundamental, $[\omega_1 = (\pi/l)(T/\mathbf{m})^{1/2}]$, with reference to the
D.E.

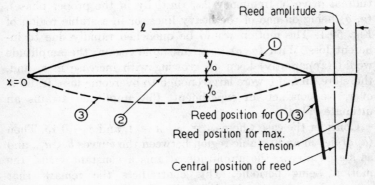

Fig. 59.2

$$d^2g/dt^2 + \omega_1^2(1 - 2\gamma \cos 2\omega_0 t)g = 0. \qquad 59.3$$

Writing y for g, $t = z/\omega_0$, $a = (\omega_1/\omega_0)^2$, $q = \gamma a$, this becomes

$$d^2y/dz^2 + (a - 2q \cos 2z)y = 0, \qquad 59.4$$

which is the canonical or standard form of Mathieu's equation [14].

The coefficient of y, namely, $(a - 2q \cos 2z)$, is periodic in z with period π, and the solution may take one of three different forms, depending upon the values of the parameters a, q. To explain these forms, we make use of the chart of Fig. 59.1A [14]. When the point (a, q) lies upon one of the curves a_0, b_1, a_1, $\cdots$, the first solution is periodic and continuous, but the second, although oscillatory, is non-periodic and $\rightarrow \pm \infty$ as $z \rightarrow + \infty$. When (a, q) lies in a region marked 'stable', both solutions are oscillatory and continuous, and may be periodic or non-periodic. When (a, q) lies in a region marked 'unstable', both solutions are oscillatory: the first tends exponentially to $\pm \infty$, and the second to zero, as $z \rightarrow + \infty$.

Practical considerations. If the string were driven *transversely* in its first mode ω_1 (no nodal point between the supports), the shape would have the form $\sin (\pi x/l)$. Suppose that during motion, the transverse drive were suddenly replaced by a longitudinal drive of frequency $2\omega_1$ (initially in the proper phase), (a, q) being on one of the heavy lines, or in a stable region of Fig. 59.1. The motion would be quenched rapidly due to inherent loss. With (a, q) in an unstable region, the amplitude would (apparently) keep on growing with increase in z, and, therefore, in t, if q were large enough to overcome loss. If, however, we conduct an experiment, the amplitude attains an ultimate value.

Consider the case where $\omega_1 = \omega_0$, $a = 1$, and $q = 0.15$. Then (a, q) lies in an unstable region between the curves b_1, a_1, and as stated above, the amplitude attains a constant value, the motion being periodic. This contradicts the remark that $y \rightarrow \pm \infty$ as $z \rightarrow + \infty$. We infer, therefore, that 59.4 needs to be modified in order to incorporate the amplitude limitation. Before investigating this point, we shall consider the motion of the string in relation to that of the reed.

Since $2\omega_0 = 2\omega_1$, the tension varies at twice the rate of vibration of the string. Referring to Fig. 59.2, (1) is the position of maximum displacement, the reed being at its extreme left where the tension has its least value $T(1 - 2\gamma)$. When the reed is at the extreme right, the tension has its largest value $T(1 + 2\gamma)$, so the string is then in mid-position as at (2). Also when the reed is next at its extreme left, the string is at (3). Thus the reed executes one cycle in the same time as the string executes half a cycle, so a subharmonic of half-frequency occurs. The string and reed may be seen in slow motion by aid of a stroboscope, and the subharmonic 'vizualised'. If the frequency variation of both reed and stroboscope is sufficiently small, the configuration of the string and reed at any instant may be 'frozen' for inspection.

To modify the D.E. we first seek some physical condition which is likely to account for the amplitude limitation. We saw in §§37, 39, that a driven system having a control $s_1 y + s_3 y^3$ (s_1 , $s_3 > 0$) does not resonate. But if we suppose that $s_3 y^3$ is relatively small, in the initial stage there will, in effect, be a quasi-resonance condition (low reactance), and the amplitude will grow until $s_3 y^3$ causes distuning by virtue of the increased stiffness. Now let us apply this notion to the present problem. The constant tension of the string is proportional to a, and if to a we add by^2, (b small > 0) 59.4 becomes

$$d^2y/dz^2 + (a + by^2 - 2q \cos 2z)y = 0. \qquad 59.5$$

The control now has the form $ay + by^3$, and 59.5 is non-linear. To effect simplification, loss has been excluded. Its inclusion entails the term $2\kappa \, dy/dz$ on the l.h.s. of 59.5.

60. SOLUTION OF 59.5   To ascertain whether this D.E. will account for the observed behaviour of the string, we have to obtain its solution. The D.E. cannot be solved exactly,* so we seek an adequate approximation. Experimental evidence indicates that the subharmonic is decidedly dominant, other frequencies which are present being relatively unimportant (q small > 0). Thus we are justified in assuming that

---

*Unless the conditions given at the end of this section are satisfied.

$y \simeq y_0 \cos z$. Substituting this into 59.5, and omitting terms in $\cos 3z$, we get

$$\left. \begin{array}{r} y'' = -y_0 \cos z \\[1mm] ay = ay_0 \cos z \\[1mm] -(2q \cos 2z)y = -qy_0 \cos z \\[1mm] by^3 = (3by_0^3 \cos z)/4. \end{array} \right\} \quad 60.1$$

Equating the coefficient of $\cos z$ to zero, we obtain

$$y_0(a - 1 - q) + 3by_0^3/4 = 0, \qquad 60.2$$

and since $y_0 \neq 0$,

$$|y_0| = \{(4/3b)(1 + q - a)\}^{1/2}, \qquad 60.3$$

which is real > 0, provided $(1 + q) > a$. Now $a = 1$, so we must have $q > 0$, and this holds when the driving agent vibrates. 60.3 shows that the amplitude is limited so long as $b > 0$, and the larger b, the smaller $|y_0|$. We have demonstrated, therefore, that amplitude limitation may be explained by a species of detuning due to non-linear control.

Since $y \simeq y_0 \cos z$, 59.5 may be expressed in the approximate form

$$d^2y/dz^2 + \{a + (by_0^2/2)(1 + \cos 2z) - 2q \cos 2z\}y = 0, \quad 60.4$$

or $d^2y/dz^2 + \{(a + by_0^2/2) - 2(q - by_0^2/4) \cos 2z\}y = 0.$ 60.5

Taking $a + by_0^2/2 = a_1$, $q - by_0^2/4 = q_1$, and using the value of y_0^2 from 60.3 gives, with $a = 1$,

$$a_1 = 1 + 2q/3, \qquad q_1 = 2q/3. \qquad 60.6$$

If $q_1 \ll 2$, the equation for the curve a_1 in Fig. 59.1B is approximately

$$a_1 = 1 + q_1, \qquad 60.7$$

and this is precisely what 60.6 entails. Hence the point (a_1, q_1)

for 60.5 lies on the curve, and so by §59 the solution is periodic (period 2π). Thus if P is the initial or starting point, as the oscillation grows, P moves gradually to P_1 on the curve a_1, when the motion is stable and the amplitude constant. In practice P_1 is just below a_1, such that inherent loss is balanced by the tendency to instability.

★*Second approximation.* Since the motion of the string is symmetrical about its central position, we take

$$y = A_1 \cos z + A_3 \cos 3z. \qquad 60.8$$

Substituting into 59.5 and equating the coefficients of $\cos z$, $\cos 3z$, to zero independently, yields two equations for A_1, A_3. Rejecting terms involving A_3^2, A_3^3, $\cos 5z$, $\cos 7z$, $\cos 9z$, in these equations, it is left for the reader to show that

$$A_3/A_1 \simeq -(2q + a - 1)/3(7 + a - 2q), \qquad 60.9$$

provided q is not too large. With $a = 1$, $q = 0.15$, 60.9 gives $A_3/A_1 \simeq -0.013$. Substituting into 60.8, the second approximation is

$$y = A_1(\cos z - 0.013 \cos 3z). \qquad 60.10$$

Thus the amplitude of the third harmonic is only 1.3 per cent that of the fundamental, so the motion is nearly cosinusoidal as in §36.

★*Comparison with valve oscillator.* If v is proportional to the variable grid potential, the D.E. for a self-oscillatory thermionic valve circuit may be expressed in the form

$$\ddot{v} - \epsilon(1 - v^2)\dot{v} + v = 0. \qquad 60.11$$

Writing $\epsilon = q$, $t = z$, $v = (3b/q)^{1/2}y$, 60.11 becomes

$$y'' - (q - 3by^2)y' + y = 0. \qquad 60.12$$

When *b and q are small*, the first approximation periodic solution is

$$y = (4q/3b)^{1/2} \cos z. \qquad 60.13^*$$

60.13 is identical with the corresponding solution of 59.5 if $a = 1$; for the r.h.s. of 60.3 is then $(4q/3b)^{1/2}$.

The damping term $-\epsilon(1 - v^2)\dot{v}$ is non-linear, in virtue of curvature of the valve characteristic. Since $v = (3b/q)^{1/2}y = 2 \cos t$, we have $-\epsilon(1 - v^2) = \epsilon(2 \cos 2t + 1)$; so the damping coefficient changes sign at twice the rate of the valve oscillation. The net loss in interval 2π is zero (periodic motion). Moreover, amplitude limitation is due to non-linear *damping*, whereas in the case of the string it is due to non-linear *control*. The transformation of 60.11, as indicated above, and the form of solution at 60.13 is left as an exercise for the reader.

As additional exercises, periodic solutions of 59.5 and 60.11 may be found by the perturbation method [15]. For 59.5 using $y(0) = A$, $y'(0) = 0$,

$$y \simeq A\{(1 + q/12 + q^2/32) \cos z$$
$$\qquad\qquad\qquad 60.14$$
$$- [(q + q^2/4)/12] \cos 3z\},$$

and
$$a \simeq (1 - 3A^2b/4 + 3A^4b^2/128)$$
$$\qquad\qquad\qquad 60.15$$
$$+ q(1 - A^2b/16) - q^2/8.$$

If $a = 1$, with b, q, small, by 60.15 we must have approximately,

$$-3A^2b/4 + q \simeq 0, \quad \text{so} \quad |A| \simeq (4q/3b)^{1/2}. \quad 60.16$$

Inserting this into 60.15, there is a remainder $-q^2/6 \simeq -0.0038$ when $q = 0.15$, which is negligible.

Take 60.11 in the form

$$\ddot{v} - \epsilon(1 - v^2)\dot{v} + av = 0, \qquad\qquad 60.17$$

and assume that [15]

$$v = v_0 + \epsilon v_1 + \epsilon^2 v_2 + \cdots, \quad a = \alpha_0 + \alpha_1\epsilon + \alpha_2\epsilon^2 + \cdots,$$

---

*When $\epsilon = q$ exceeds a certain value, the solution contains important higher harmonic terms, and 60.13 cannot be applied. The comparison of the two D.E. pertains to $0 < \epsilon = q \ll 1$.

$v(0) = A, \dot{v}(0) = 0$. Then with $\psi = \omega t$, we find that $A = 2$,

$$v \simeq (2 - 13\epsilon^2/96\omega_0^2) \cos \psi - (\epsilon/4\omega_0)(3 \sin \psi - \sin 3\psi)$$

$$\hspace{4cm} 60.18$$

$$+ (\epsilon^2/96\omega_0^2)(18 \cos 3\psi - 5 \cos 5\psi),$$

and
$$\omega_0^2 \simeq a - \epsilon^2/8, \hspace{2cm} 60.19$$

so with $a = 1$, $\hspace{1cm} \omega_0 \simeq 1 - \epsilon^2/16$. $\hspace{2cm}$ 60.20

★*Exact solution of* 59.5. Retaining the cos $3z$ terms in 60.1, with b, $q > 0$, leads to

$$y_0(a - 1 - q + 3by_0^2/4) \cos z$$

$$\hspace{4cm} 60.21$$

$$- y_0(q - by_0^2/4) \cos 3z = 0.$$

For $y_0 \cos z$ to be an exact solution, the coefficients of cos z, cos $3z$ must vanish. Hence

$$(a - 1 - q + 3by_0^2/4) = 0, \quad \text{and} \quad (q - by_0^2/4) = 0. \hspace{1cm} 60.22$$

The second gives $\hspace{1cm} y_0 = \pm 2(q/b)^{1/2}, \hspace{2cm}$ 60.23

and on inserting this in the first, we get

$$a = (1 - 2q). \hspace{2cm} 60.24$$

Then there are two subharmonic solutions of opposite phase, namely

$$y = \pm 2(q/b)^{\frac{1}{2}} \cos z, \hspace{2cm} 60.25$$

which are stable provided q is not too large. If the string is always taut, $a > 0$, so from 60.23, 60.24, $0 < q < 0.5$, and the solutions are stable. It is left to the reader to show that when $b < 0$, $a = 1 + 2q$, y_0 as in 60.23, b being taken positive therein, while $y = y_0 \sin z$.

CHAPTER VI

Longitudinal and Torsional Vibration of Uniform Bars and Tubes

61. BAR OR TUBE Longitudinal vibration in this case is akin to sound waves in an organ pipe. The particles of the bar move to and fro parallel to the axis, assumed linear. The cyclical extension and compression entail lateral deformation (remembering Poisson's ratio), but this may be ignored if the wavelength of sound† in the bar is long compared with its cross-sectional dimensions.

We derive the D.E. under conditions (a)-(e) in §50. Since the modulus of elasticity E = stress/strain, if the stress at x in Fig. 61.1A is F, and the extension of dx is $d\xi$, we have

$$E = F/(\partial\xi/\partial x), \qquad \text{or} \qquad F = E\partial\xi/\partial x, \qquad 61.1$$

so the force per unit length at x is

$$A_s\partial F/\partial x = A_s E\partial^2\xi/\partial x^2, \qquad 61.2$$

A_s being the cross-sectional area. By d'Alembert's principle

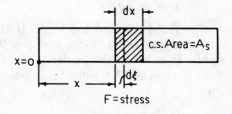

Fig. 61.1A

---

†Wavelength = 2π velocity/ω, i.e. $\lambda = 2\pi c/\omega$.

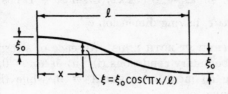

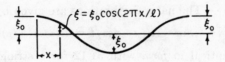

Fig. 61.1B

(§75), the r.h.s. of 61.2 is equal to the accelerational force per unit length, i.e. $A_s \rho \partial^2 \xi / \partial t^2$, ρ being the density of the bar. Equating these two, and taking $c^2 = E/\rho$, we obtain

$$\partial^2 \xi / \partial x^2 = (1/c^2) \partial^2 \xi / \partial t^2, \qquad 61.3$$

which is identical in form with 51.5, the D.E. for the *transverse* vibration of a uniform string. The dimension of the l.h.s. is l^{-1}, while that of $\partial^2 \xi / \partial t^2$ is lt^{-2}. Hence for like dimensions on each side of 61.3,* c must represent a velocity lt^{-1}. It is the velocity of propagation of sound waves of small amplitude along the bar, being independent of frequency. The general solution of 61.3 is 54.1, and the remarks concerning wave motion on strings in §54 apply equally to longitudinal waves in bars or tubes.

As in §51, the appropriate solution of 61.3 is

$$\xi(x, t) = f(x)g(t)$$

---

*The dimensions of all terms in the D.E. for a physical system must be the same.

$$= (A \sin kx + B \cos kx)(C \sin \omega t + D \cos \omega t), \qquad 61.4$$

where $k = \omega/c$, having dimension l^{-1}.

62. BAR FREE AT BOTH ENDS Absence of stress at the ends entails the boundary conditions (i), (ii) $\partial \xi / \partial x = 0$, at $x = 0, l$. Substituting (i) into 61.4 gives $A = 0$, while (ii) yields the frequency equation

$$\sin kl = 0, \qquad \text{so} \qquad kl = n\pi, \qquad 62.1$$

$n = 1, 2, \cdots$. The natural vibrations are given by

$$\omega_n l/c = n\pi, \qquad \text{or} \qquad \omega_n = nc\pi/l = (n\pi/l)(E/\rho)^{1/2}, \qquad 62.2$$

which is identical in *form* with 51.12 for a string of length l. Since by 62.1, $k_n = n\pi/l$, and also $A = 0$, B arbitrary, by substituting into 61.4 and omitting the time factor, the amplitude at any x for the nth mode is

$$\xi_n(x) = \xi_l \cos (n\pi x/l), \qquad 62.3$$

ξ_l being an arbitrary amplitude at $x = l$. When $x = (2m - 1)l/2n$, $n \geq 1$, $m \leq n$, $\xi_n = 0$ and n nodes occur *between* the ends of the bar (Fig. 61.1B). The periodic time is $2l/nc$, this being the interval of travel from a node to the next but one, i.e. a distance of a wavelength, as in the case of the string in §51. The overtones are harmonic, having the ratios 2, 3, 4, $\cdots$, to the frequency of the fundamental.

63. FIXED-FREE BAR The b.c. are (i) $\xi = 0$, $x = 0$, (ii) $\partial \xi / \partial x = 0$, $x = l$, since there is no stress at the free end. Using these in 61.4 leads to the frequency equation

$$\cos kl = 0, \qquad \text{so} \qquad kl = (2n - 1)\pi/2, \qquad 63.1$$

$n = 1, 2, \cdots$, and

$$\omega_n = (2n - 1)\pi c/2l; \qquad 63.2$$

also $\qquad \xi_n(x) = \xi_l \sin \{(2n - 1)\pi x/2l\}, \qquad 63.3$

ξ_l being an arbitrary amplitude at $x = l$. When $x =$

$2ml/(2n - 1)$, $n \geq 2$, $m < n$, $\xi_n = 0$, and $(n - 1)$ nodes occur in $0 < x < l$. There is no node for $n = 1$; that for $n = 2$ occurs at $x = 2l/3$. By 63.2 the periodic time is $4l/(2n - 1)c$, which is four times the interval of travel from the node nearest the end of the bar to that end, i.e. a distance equal to the wavelength. The overtones are harmonic, their frequency ratios to the fundamental being 3, 5, 7, $\cdots$, the even harmonics not occurring.

64. FIXED-FIXED BAR   The b.c. are (1) $\xi = 0$, $x = 0$, (ii) $\xi = 0$, $x = l$, which yield the frequency equation $\sin kl = 0$, and as at 62.2 the natural vibrations are given by

$$\omega_n = nc\pi/l; \qquad\qquad 64.1$$

also $$\xi_n(x) = \xi_0 \sin (n\pi x/l), \qquad\qquad 64.2$$

ξ_0 being an arbitrary amplitude at $x = l/2n$. When $x = ml/n$, $n \geq 2$, $\dot{m} < n$, $\xi_n = 0$, and $(n - 1)$ nodes occur *between* the clamps. It follows from 62.2, 64.1 that the natural frequencies of free-free and fixed-fixed bars of equal length and material are identical. The remarks at the end of §62 are relevant here.

65. FORCED VIBRATION OF FIXED-FREE BAR   It is driven axially at $x = l$ by a force $fe^{i\omega t}$ per unit area of cross-section. The b.c. are (i) $\xi = 0$, $x = 0$, (ii) $E\partial\xi/\partial x = fe^{i\omega t}$ at $x = l$. Since C, D in 61.4 are arbitrary, for the forced vibration we may put $C = i$, $D = 1$, and then

$$\xi(x, t) = (A \sin kx + B \cos kx)e^{i\omega t}. \qquad\qquad 65.1$$

(i) gives $B = 0$, so

$$\xi = A \sin kxe^{i\omega t}, \qquad\qquad 65.2$$

and $$\partial\xi/\partial x = Ak \cos kxe^{i\omega t}, \qquad\qquad 65.3$$

so from (ii) $$A' = f/kE \cos kl. \qquad\qquad 65.4$$

Therefore, by 65.2, 65.4, taking the real part of the time factor,

$$\xi(x, t) = \{\mathbf{f}/\omega(\rho E)^{1/2}\}(\sin kx/\cos kl)\cos \omega t, \qquad 65.5$$

which is identical in form with 55.2 for the transversely driven string. ξ has infinities when $\cos kl = 0$, so $kl = (2n - 1)\pi/2$, and by §63 the corresponding values of ω_n give the natural vibrations.

Input or driving point impedance. By definition

$$z = \text{force/velocity} = \mathbf{f}A_s e^{i\omega t}/\dot{\xi}(l, t), \qquad 65.6$$

where A_s is the c-s area. From 65.5 with $e^{i\omega t}$ for $\cos \omega t$,

$$\dot{\xi}_l = i\{\mathbf{f}/(\rho E)^{1/2}\}\tan kle^{i\omega t} \qquad 65.7$$

so $$z = -iA_s(\rho E)^{1/2}\cot kl, \qquad 65.8$$

which has zeros when $\dot{\xi}_l$ has infinities and vice-versa, being identical in form with 55.5 for a transversely driven string.

★66. FORCE APPLIED SUDDENLY   Suppose a tensile force $\mathbf{f}$ per unit area is applied to the free end of a fixed-free bar at $t = 0$. What is the longitudinal displacement $\xi(x, t)$? The D.E. is 61.3 which has to be solved for the initial conditions (a) $\xi = 0$, $t = 0$, $0 \le x < l$, (b) $\dot{\xi} = 0$, $t = 0$, $0 \le x < l$, and the b.c. (i) $\xi = 0$, $x = 0$, (ii) $E\partial\xi/\partial x = \mathbf{f}$ at $x = l$. The simplest procedure is operational calculus [13]. Then with $\xi(x, t) \Rightarrow \phi(x, p)$, the transform equation for 61.3 is

$$d^2\phi/dx^2 - \lambda^2\phi = 0, \qquad 66.1$$

$\lambda = p/c$, there being no terms on the r.h.s., in virtue of initial quiescence. The complete solution of 66.1 is

$$\phi = A \sinh \lambda x + B \cosh \lambda x. \qquad 66.2$$

Now $\phi(x, p) = p \int_0^\infty e^{-pt}\xi(x, t)\, dt$, so for b.c. (i), $\phi = 0$ when $x = 0$. Also if differentiation under the integral sign is valid,

$$d\phi/dx = p \int_0^\infty e^{-pt}(\partial\xi/\partial x)\, dt. \qquad 66.3$$

For b.c. (ii), $\partial\xi/\partial x = \mathbf{f}/E$, so $d\phi/dx$ has this value at $x = l$.

Applying these transform b.c. to 66.2, gives $B = 0$, and $A = $ $f/\lambda E \cosh \lambda l$. Inserting A, B into 66.2 yields

$$\phi(x, p) = (f/E\lambda)(\sinh \lambda x/\cosh \lambda l), \qquad 66.4$$

which is the transform solution. To invert this we shall use the Mellin theorem [12]. Thus with $\lambda = z/c$

$$\xi(x, t) = \{(fc/E)/2\pi i\} \int_{c-i\infty}^{c+i\infty} e^{zt} \sinh (zx/c) \, dz/z^2 \cosh (zl/c). \quad 66.5$$

The singularities of the integrand are simple poles, and a limit point for the poles as $z \to \infty$. The poles occur when $z = 0$, and when $\cosh zl/c = \cos (izl/c) = 0$, i.e. $izl/c = \pm(2n + 1)\pi/2$, $n = 0, 1, 2, \cdots$, or $z = \pm i(2n + 1)\pi c/2l$. All these poles are on the axis of imaginaries. It may be shown that the integral in 66.5 taken round a large semicircle of radius r_m on the left of the contour $c \pm i\infty$ $(c > 0)$, which meets it *between* the mth and $(m + 1)$th poles, tends to zero as $r_m \to +\infty$. Accordingly the value of the integral is obtained by summing the residues at the poles.

When $z \to 0$, the integrand $\to (x/c)/z$, so the residue is x/c, and the contribution to the integral is fx/E. To sum the residues at the poles on the imaginary axis, we proceed as shown below [12]:

$\sum$ residues

$$= \sum_{n=0}^{\infty} \left\{ \frac{e^{zt} \sinh (zx/c)}{d\{z^2 \cosh (zl/c)\}/dz} \right\}_{z=\pm i(2n+1)\pi c/2l} \qquad 66.6$$

$$= \sum_{n=0}^{\infty} \left\{ \frac{e^{zt} \sinh (zx/c)}{(z^2 l/c) \sinh (zl/c) + 2z \cosh (zl/c)} \right\}_{z=\pm i(2n+1)\pi c/2l} \qquad 66.7$$

$$= -(4l/\pi^2 c) \sum_{n=0}^{\infty} [(-1)^n/(2n + 1)^2] \sin \{(2n + 1)\pi x/2l\}$$

$$\cdot [e^{i(2n+1)\pi ct/2l} + e^{-i(2n+1)\pi ct/2l}] \qquad 66.8$$

$$= -(8l/\pi^2 c) \sum_{n=1}^{\infty} [(-1)^{n-1}/(2n-1)^2] \sin \{(2n-1)\pi x/2l\}$$

66.9

$$\cdot \cos \{(2n-1)\pi c t/2l\}.$$

Multiplying 66.9 by fc/E and adding the contribution from the pole at $z = 0$, yields $(0 \leq x \leq l)$

$$\xi(x, t) = (f/E)[x - (8l/\pi^2) \sum_{n=1}^{\infty} \frac{(-1)^{n-1}}{(2n-1)^2}$$

66.10

$$\sin \{(2n-1)\pi x/2l\} \cos \{(2n-1)\pi ct/2l\}].$$

The sigma term represents an infinity of vibrational modes (whose frequencies are the same as those in §63), due to the impulsing effect when f is applied at $t = 0$. In practice where loss occurs, these would be extinguished quickly, leaving the static elongation fx/E. This *type* of result is quite general, for when a change occurs in the loading of a continuous system, its natural vibrations are excited. By virtue of the factor $1/(2n-1)^2$, the amplitudes of the (harmonic) overtones fall off inversely as the squares of their orders. The frequencies of the harmonics have the ratios 3, 5, $\cdots$, to that of the fundamental.

★67. WAVEFORM REPRESENTED BY 66.10 AT $x = l$ The expression is then

$$\xi(l, t)$$

67.1

$$= (fl/E)[1 - (8/\pi^2) \sum_{n=1}^{\infty} \cos \{(2n-1)\pi ct/2l\}/(2n-1)^2],$$

and by [13, p. 206, ex. 6] the waveform is that of Fig. 67.1. The static elongation fl/E is the mean displacement, but the maximum being twice this, we infer that the sudden loading of the bar (without shock) causes twice the static strain (and stress)— see end of §30. The first maximum at B occurs when $t = 2l/c$.

Starting at $t = 0$, $x = l$, the impulse travels along the bar with velocity c, so the extension at $x = l$ increases linearly with time as shown by OA in Fig. 67.1, where $t = l/c$ when it reaches the clamp. The impulse is then reflected back, and in travelling down the bar, gradually increases the extension as shown by AB. The effect of **f** and its reflection are additive, so when $t = 2l/c$ the displacement and, therefore, the strain and stress

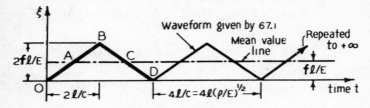

Fig. 67.1

have double their normal statical values. The displacement now being a maximum, so also is the potential or strain energy, and the end of the bar is momentarily at rest. It then begins to move backwards, until at C the equilibrium position is reached, but in virtue of momentum, the motion continues to D, and so on. We remark that however slowly the load is applied, oscillation will ensue, but its character depends upon the applied force-time relationship.

★68. IMPULSIVE AXIAL BLOW AT $x = l$ We take the rectangular impulse of Fig. 29.1. This is the same as a force **f** applied for a time interval h, the strength of the impulse being **f**h per unit cross-sectional area. To obtain the rectangular form, we suppose $+$**f** to be applied from $t = (0, +\infty)$, and $-$**f** from $t = (h, +\infty)$. Then b.c. (ii) in §66 becomes $\partial\xi/\partial x = (\mathbf{f}/E)\{H(t) - H(t - h)\}$, where $H(t)$ is Heaviside's unit or step function. It follows that the transform b.c. is $d\phi/dx = (\mathbf{f}/E)(1 - e^{-ph})$ at $x = l$, so by 66.4

$$\phi(x, p) = (\mathbf{f}c/Ep)(1 - e^{-ph}) \sinh (px/c)/\cosh (pl/c). \quad 68.1$$

Thus

$$\xi(l, t) = \frac{(\mathbf{f}c/E)}{2\pi i} \int_{c-i\infty}^{c+i\infty} \{e^{zt} - e^{z(t-h)}\} \frac{\sinh (zl/c)\,dz}{z^2 \cosh (zl/c)}, \quad 68.2$$

and by 66.9 with $x = l$,

$$\xi(l,\ t) = -(fl/E)(8/\pi^2) \sum_{n=1}^{\infty} [\cos \{(2n - 1)\pi ct/2l\} \tag{68.3}$$

$$- \cos \{(2n - 1)\pi c(t - h)/2l\}]/(2n - 1)^2$$

$$= (16fl/\pi^2 E) \sum_{n=1}^{\infty} \sin \{(2n - 1)\pi c(t - h/2)/2l\} \tag{68.4}$$

$$\cdot \sin \{(2n - 1)\pi ch/4l\}/(2n - 1)^2,$$

for $t > h$. This vanishes if $h = 4ml/c$, $m = 1, 2, \cdots$, because the force is removed at a time instant when the bar is quiescent. In the interval $0 < t < h$, it is obvious that 66.10 applies.

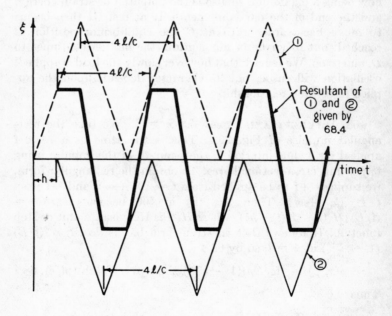

Fig. 68.1

$(f/E)H(t)$ yields the waveform (1) in Fig. 68.1 (obtained from Fig. 67.1), while $(f/E)H(t - h)$ yields the same waveform inverted and commencing at $t = h$, as shown by (2). The resultant waveform is that due to the impulse, and it is indicated by the heavy solid line. For a compressive impulse, this would have to be reversed in sign.

★69. **f** cos ωt APPLIED AT $t = 0$, $x = l$ The transform solution is obtained on replacing the L.T. of **f** i.e. f, by that of **f** cos ωt, namely, $fp^2/(p^2 + \omega^2)$, in 66.4, so

$$\phi(x, p) = \{fcp/E(p^2 + \omega^2)\} \sinh (px/c)/\cosh (pl/c), \qquad 69.1$$

and corresponding to 66.5, we get

$$\xi(x, t) = \frac{fc/E}{2\pi i} \int_{c-i\infty}^{c+i\infty} \frac{e^{zt} \sinh (zx/c) \, dz}{(z - i\omega)(z + i\omega) \cosh (zl/c)}. \qquad 69.2$$

The integrand has simple poles* at $z = \pm i\omega$, $z = \pm i(2n - 1)\pi c/2l$, $n = 1, 2, \cdots$. Evaluating the residues at these poles leads to the solution

$$\xi(x, t) = (fl/E)\left[\frac{\sin kx}{kl \cos kl} \cos \omega t - (8/\pi^2) \sum_{n=1}^{\infty} (-1)^{n-1} \right.$$

$$69.3$$

$$\left. \cdot \frac{\sin \{(2n - 1)\pi x/2l\} \cos \{(2n - 1)\pi ct/2l\}}{(2n - 1)^2 - (2kl/\pi)^2} \right].$$

where $k = \omega/c$. The first term is similar in form to 55.2 and represents the forced oscillation, while the sigma term represents the natural oscillations due to the (sudden) application of the driving force at $t = 0$. Their frequencies are identical with those in §66, but their amplitudes are now greater in the ratio $(2n - 1)^2/\{(2n - 1)^2 - (2kl/\pi)^2\} = 1/[1 - \{2kl/(2n - 1)\pi\}^2]$. When $\omega \to 0$, the driving force $\to$ **f**, and 69.3 $\to$ 66.10, a result the reader should verify.

---

*Provided $\omega \neq (2n - 1)\pi c/2l$, i.e. $2kl/\pi \neq (2n - 1)$, and 69.3 is valid under this condition. Otherwise double poles occur at which special evaluation is needed.

70. UNIFORM COIL SPRING Referring to Fig. 61.1, the force at any point x on the spring is given by

$$f = s \times \text{strain} = s\partial\xi/\partial x, \qquad 70.1$$

where s is the stiffness *per unit length*,* i.e. the force per unit displacement for unit length of spring. Thus

$$\partial f/\partial x = s\partial^2\xi/\partial x^2, \qquad 70.2$$

and the difference in force across an element of length dx is

$$\partial f = s(\partial^2\xi/\partial x^2)\, dx. \qquad 70.3$$

The accelerational force is $m(\partial^2\xi/\partial t^2)\, dx$, so by equating this to 70.3,

we obtain $\qquad \partial^2\xi/\partial x^2 = (1/c^2)\partial^2\xi/\partial t^2, \qquad 70.4$

where $c = (s/m)^{1/2}$, the velocity of propagation of a disturbance along the spring, independent of frequency.† 70.4 is identical in *form* with 51.5 for the transverse vibration of a string, and 61.3 for the longitudinal vibration of a bar. It follows, therefore, that the results in §§61-69 apply to the uniform coil spring, provided the formulae for c^2 are interchanged. During vibration there are nodes on a spring as in the case of a bar under similar boundary conditions.

71. LOADED SPRING One end is anchored and a mass m attached at $x = l$, the free end. (See Fig. 2.1A). The problem is to determine the natural frequencies of the system. Omitting the time factor, by 61.4 the formal solution is

$$\xi(x) = A \sin kx + B \cos kx, \qquad 71.1$$

where $k = \omega/c = \omega(m/s)^{1/2}$. The b.c. are (i) $\xi = 0$, $x = 0$, (ii) $s\partial\xi/\partial x = -m\partial^2\xi/\partial t^2 = m\omega^2\xi$ at $x = l$. The first b.c. gives $B = 0$, and for the second

---

*If the stiffness of a spring length l is s, that of unit length is ls.

†For a spring of length l, $(s/m)^{1/2} = (sl^2/ml)^{1/2} = $ (stiffness/mass of spring)$^{1/2} \times$ length.

$$(\partial \xi / \partial x)_{x=l} = Ak \cos kl = A(m\omega^2/\mathbf{s}) \sin kl. \qquad 71.2$$

Since $A \neq 0$, for the frequency equation we must have

$$\tan kl = \mathbf{s}k/m\omega^2 = \mathbf{s}k^2 l/kl\omega^2 m, \qquad 71.3$$

or $\qquad\qquad \lambda \tan \lambda = m_s/m = \varphi, \qquad\qquad 71.4$

with $\lambda = kl$, and m_s the mass of the spring. If $m_s \ll m$, for the smallest root of 71.4, λ will be small, and we may write $\tan \lambda \simeq \lambda + \lambda^3/3$, so

$$\lambda^2 + \lambda^4/3 = \varphi. \qquad 71.5$$

Solving this and using the binomial expansion, we get

$$\lambda^2 \simeq \varphi(1 - \varphi/3), \qquad 71.6$$

so $\qquad\qquad \omega_1^2(\mathbf{m/s})l^2 \simeq (\mathbf{m}l/m)(1 - \varphi/3). \qquad 71.7$

Hence the fundamental frequency of vibration is

$$\omega_1^2 \simeq s/\{m(1 + \varphi/3)\} = s/(m + m_s/3), \qquad 71.8$$

where $s = \mathbf{s}/l$, the stiffness of the *whole* spring. 71.8 reproduces 12.4, which was derived from energy considerations.

For a given φ, the transcendental equation 71.4 has an infinity of positive roots λ_n, $n = 1, 2, 3, \cdots$, each of which corresponds to a mode whose frequency is given by $k_n = \lambda_n/l$, or $\omega_n = (\lambda_n/l)(\mathbf{s/m})^{1/2}$.

72. THE HIGHER MODES When φ/λ in 71.4 is small enough, we may write the frequency equation in the approximate form

$$\tan \lambda \simeq 0, \qquad \text{or} \qquad \sin kl \simeq 0. \qquad 72.1$$

Thus $\qquad\qquad \lambda_n \simeq n\pi, \qquad \text{or} \qquad k \simeq n\pi/l, \qquad (n \geq 1) \qquad 72.2$

and for a given n, the accuracy increases with decrease in φ. By §64 this is the frequency equation for a spring fixed at *both* ends. The physical explanation is that nodes occur on the spring, and as the frequency increases, the distance between m

and the nearest node decreases. Thus the *relative* inertia effect
of *m* increases, being greater than that for the fundamental

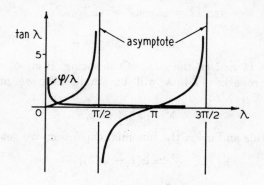

Fig. 72.1

vibration when the displacement of the spring is nearly in phase
throughout its length. Hence as ω_n increases, the condition at
m tends to simulate that of fixation. There are standing waves
on the spring for any $n > 1$, which occur by virtue of reflection
at *m* and the end $x = 0$.

The solution of 71.4 is illustrated by the graphs in Fig. 72.1,
where the roots occur at the intersections of $y = \tan \lambda$ and
$y = \varphi/\lambda$. In the case $\varphi = 0.09$, $\lambda_1 \simeq 0.296$, and the remaining
intersections are close to the points $\lambda = n\pi$.

73. TORSIONAL VIBRATION OF CIRCULAR BAR OR TUBE Consider an element of the bar, length dx under torsion (Fig. 73.1),
the twisting moment at any point x is $GI_s(\partial\theta/\partial x)$, where G is
the shear modulus, and I_s the polar m.o.i. of the uniform *cross-
section*. The net moment on dx is

$$\frac{\partial}{\partial x}(GI_s\partial\theta/\partial x)\,dx = GI_s(\partial^2\theta/\partial x^2)\,dx. \qquad 73.1$$

The inertial torque is, by 10.6, the product of the m.o.i. of dx
and the angular acceleration, namely,

$$\rho I_s(\partial^2\theta/\partial t^2)\ dx. \qquad 73.2$$

Equating 73.1, 73.2, yields the D.E.

$$\partial^2\theta/\partial x^2 = (1/c^2)\partial^2\theta/\partial t^2, \qquad 73.3$$

where $c = (G/\rho)^{1/2}$ is the velocity of torsional waves along the

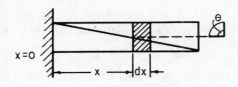

Fig. 73.1

bar, independent of ω. This is identical in *form* with 51.5, 61.3, 70.4. Hence the results in §§62-64 apply in the present case if G is written for E.

74. Bar loaded at free end by disk   We refer to §10 where the b.c. are (i) $\theta = 0$, $x = 0$, (ii) $GI_s(\partial\theta/\partial x)_{x=l} = -\mathbf{I}(\partial^2\theta/\partial t^2)_{x=l}$, the twisting moment at $x = l$. Thus if $\theta(l, t) = \theta_0 e^{i\omega t}$, (ii) may be written $(\partial\theta/\partial x)_{x=l} = \omega^2\mathbf{I}\theta_0/GI_s$. Using the form of solution at 61.4 without the time factor, we have

$$\theta(x) = A \sin kx + B \cos kx. \qquad 74.1$$

(i) gives $B = 0$, and by (ii)

$$A = \omega^2\mathbf{I}\theta_0/GI_s k \cos kl, \qquad 74.2$$

so from 74.1,

$$\theta(l) = \theta_0 = (\omega^2\mathbf{I}\theta_0/GI_s k) \tan kl. \qquad 74.3$$

Now $\omega^2 = k^2 G/\rho$, so

$$\omega^2\mathbf{I}/GI_s k = \mathbf{I}kl/\rho I_s l = kl/\alpha, \qquad 74.4$$

where $\alpha = $ (m.o.i. of whole shaft)/(m.o.i. of disk). Thus by

74.3, 74.4, the frequency equation is

$$\lambda \tan \lambda = \alpha, \qquad 74.5$$

with $\lambda = kl$, which is the same form of transcendental equation as 71.4. If $\alpha \ll 1$, by 71.6, with $k_1 = \omega_1/c_1$

$$\lambda_1^2 = \omega_1^2 l^2/c^2 \simeq \alpha/(1 + \alpha/3). \qquad 74.6$$

From 10.2, $\gamma = GI_s/l$, and since $G = \rho c^2$, we obtain $\gamma l^2/c^2 = \rho I_s l = I_s$, so $\alpha = \gamma l^2/c^2 I$. Substituting this into 74.6 leads to

$$\omega_1^2 \simeq \gamma/(I + I_s/3), \qquad 74.7$$

which agrees with the result at 14.7 obtained from energy considerations. The remarks in §72 apply equally, *mutatis mutandis*, to the present problem. When $n > 1$ there are nodal sections on the shaft, and as ω_n increases, the condition at the disk tends to simulate fixation. Torsion waves pass to and fro along the shaft, and are reflected from the ends thereby causing a standing wave pattern accompanied by nodal sections. If a driving torque is applied to a circular shaft, the displacement-time relationship may be found in the same manner as in previous sections dealing with forced oscillations. The application of the driving torque at $t = 0$, is accompanied by an infinite set of natural torsional vibrations whose relative amplitudes depend upon the waveform of the applied torque.

CHAPTER VII

Transverse Vibration of Bars and Tubes

75. DERIVATION OF D.E. The analysis is based upon the hypotheses (a)-(e) in §50, together with the following: (f) the length is large compared with the cross-sectional dimensions, (g) rotatory inertia is negligible, (h) shear displacement due to vibrational forces is negligible, (j) vibration occurs in one of the principal planes of bending. At any section distant x from the origin (Fig. 75.1), the D.E. for the static displacement is [5, 19, 20, 22],

$$EI\partial^2\xi/\partial x^2 = -M,$$
75.1

where EI is the flexural rigidity, E the elastic modulus, I the m.o.i. of the *section* about a line through the centroid in the

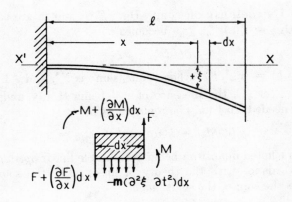

ξ is positive below X'X

Fig. 75.1

plane of bending, and perpendicular to the axis, and M the bending moment at x. The shearing force at x is

$$F = \partial M / \partial x, \qquad 75.2$$

so $\qquad -\partial F / \partial x = -\partial^2 M / \partial x^2 = \dfrac{\partial^2}{\partial x^2} (EI \partial^2 \xi / \partial x^2). \qquad 75.3$

We now apply d'Alembert's principle, which states that the vibrating bar may be considered to be loaded by inertia forces which vary along its length. If $\mathbf{m}$ is the mass per unit length (which may be variable) at x, the corresponding inertia or accelerational force is $-\mathbf{m} \partial^2 \xi / \partial t^2$. This provides the loading, so we equate it to the distance rate of loading in 75.3, thereby obtaining

$$\frac{\partial^2}{\partial x^2} (EI \partial^2 \xi / \partial x^2) = -\mathbf{m} \partial^2 \xi / \partial t^2. \qquad 75.4$$

The bending and shear which occur during transverse vibration entail two more b.c. than for longitudinal vibration. Consequently a fourth order D.E. in x is required.

76. UNIFORM BAR OR TUBE   Here E, I, and $\mathbf{m}$ are constant, so with $\xi = \xi_1(x) e^{i \omega t}$, 75.4 becomes

$$d^4 \xi / dx^4 - k^4 \xi = 0, \qquad 76.1$$

where $k^4 = \mathbf{m} \omega^2 / EI$, whose dimension* is l^{-4}, and ξ has been written for ξ_1, the presence of $e^{i \omega t}$ being tacitly understood, when needed. 76.1 may be replaced by

$$(d^2 / dx^2 - k^2)(d^2 / dx^2 + k^2) \xi = 0, \qquad 76.2$$

the bracketed quantities being permutable linear *operators*, and in accordance with the theory of linear D.E. the solution of 76.1 is the sum of the solutions of

---

*The dimensions of all terms in the D.E. for a physical system must be alike. Writing 76.1 in the form $(d^4 / dx^4 - k^4) \xi = 0$, k^4 must have dimension x^{-4}, i.e. l^{-4}.

$$d^2\xi/dx^2 - k^2\xi = 0, \quad \text{and} \quad d^2\xi/dx^2 + k^2\xi = 0. \quad 76.3$$

Hence

$$\xi(x) = A \cosh kx + B \sinh kx + C \cos kx + D \sin kx. \quad 76.4$$

Four b.c. are needed for the determination of the arbitrary constants $A - D$.

77. UNIFORM BAR CLAMPED AT $x = 0$, OTHERWISE FREE The b.c. are (i) $\xi = 0$, $x = 0$, (ii) $d\xi/dx = 0$, $x = 0$, i.e. zero slope,

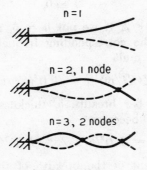

Fig. 77.1.

(iii) $d^2\xi/dx^2 = 0$, $x = l$, i.e. zero bending moment, (iv) $d^3\xi/dx^3 = 0$, $x = l$, i.e. zero shearing force. Inserting (i) into 76.4 gives

$$A + C = 0, \quad \text{or} \quad C = -A. \quad 77.1$$

Using (ii) gives

$$k(B + D) = 0, \quad \text{or} \quad D = -B. \quad 77.2$$

Substituting from 77.1, 77.2, into 76.4, we get

$$\xi = A(\cosh kx - \cos kx) + B(\sinh kx - \sin kx), \quad 77.3$$

so

$$(d^2\xi/dx^2)_{x=l} = k^2\{A(C + c) + B(S + s)\} = 0, \quad 77.4$$

and

$$(d^3\xi/dx^3)_{x=l} = k^3\{A(S - s) + B(C + c)\} = 0, \quad 77.5$$

with* $C = \cosh kl$, $c = \cos kl$, etc. Equating values of A/B from 77.4, 77.5,

yields $$(C + c)^2 = (S^2 - s^2). \qquad 77.6$$

Expanding 77.6 leads to the frequency equation

$$Cc = -1, \quad \text{or} \quad \cos kl = -1/\cosh kl. \qquad 77.7$$

The first five roots of this equation are $k_1 l \simeq 1.875$, $k_2 l \simeq 4.694$, $k_3 l \simeq 7.853$, $k_4 l \simeq 10.996$, $k_5 l \simeq 14.137$. When $kl > 14.137$, 77.7 may be written in the approximate form

$$\cos kl \simeq 0, \qquad 77.8$$

so $k_n l \simeq (2n - 1)\pi/2$. If we put $n = 5$, the above value of $k_5 l$ is obtained. The corresponding frequencies may be calculated from the formula

$$\omega_n = k_n^2 (EI/\mathbf{m})^{1/2} = (k_n l)^2 (EI/\mathbf{m}l^4)^{1/2}. \qquad 77.9$$

For a rectangular bar breadth b, thickness a, $I = ba^3/12$, $\mathbf{m}l^4 = \rho bal^4$, so 77.9 becomes

$$\omega_n = (k_n l)^2 (a/2\sqrt{3}l^2)(E/\rho)^{1/2}, \qquad 77.10$$

which is independent of the breadth of the bar, but varies inversely as the square of its length. The ratios of the frequencies of the overtones to that of the fundamental are $(k_n/k_1)^2 \simeq 6.27$, 17.55, 34.4, 56.8. The frequencies ω_2, ω_3, $\cdots$, cannot be regarded as harmonics, because their ratios to the fundamental are non-integral. They are called *enharmonic* overtones. When a tuning fork is struck, the initial tone tends to be shrill, since the overtones are enharmonic. They are damped out quickly due to loss, and ultimately little but the fundamental is audible. The shape of the bar during vibration is depicted in Fig. 77.1.

78. UNIFORM BAR FIXED AT BOTH ENDS The b.c. are (i) $\xi = 0$, $x = 0$, (ii) $d\xi/dx = 0$, $x = 0$, (iii) $\xi = 0$, $x = l$, (iv)

*Here and in subsequent sections this abbreviation has been adopted. It must not be confused with the arbitrary constant C in 76.4, 77.1, 78.1.

$d\xi/dx = 0$, $x = l$. Substituting (i), (ii) into 76.4, gives

$$C = -A, \qquad D = -B, \qquad 78.1$$

and we get 77.3. Then application of (iii), (iv) to 77.3 yields

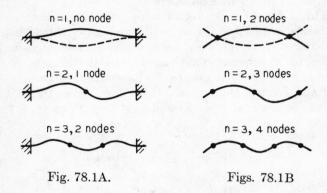

n=1, no node   n=1, 2 nodes

n=2, 1 node   n=2, 3 nodes

n=3, 2 nodes   n=3, 4 nodes

Fig. 78.1A.   Figs. 78.1B

$A(C - c) + B(S - s) = 0$, and $A(S - s) + B(C - c) = 0$. 78.2

Equating the values of A/B in 78.2, we obtain

$$(S^2 - s^2)/(C - c)^2 = 1, \qquad \text{or} \qquad 1 - Cc = 0, \qquad 78.3$$

which gives the frequency equation

$$\cos kl = 1/\cosh kl. \qquad 78.4$$

The first five roots of this equation are $k_0 l = 0$, $k_1 l \simeq 4.730$, $k_2 l \simeq 7.853$, $k_3 l \simeq 10.996$, $k_4 l \simeq 14.137$; also $k_n l \simeq (2n + 1)\pi/2$, $n \geq 5$. When $n \geq 3$, these are almost the same as the $(n + 1)$th roots of 77.7, which apply to a bar of equal length and section fixed at one end and free at the other. As in §77, the overtones are enharmonic. $k_0 l = 0$, signifies absence of motion. The shape of the bar is illustrated in Fig. 78.1A.

79. UNIFORM BAR FREE AT BOTH ENDS The b.c. are (i) $d^2\xi/dx^2 = 0$, $x = 0$, (ii) $d^3\xi/dx^3 = 0$, $x = 0$, (iii) $d^2\xi/dx^2 = 0$, $x = l$, (iv) $d^3\xi/dx^3 = 0$, $x = l$. Applying these to 76.4, the frequency equation is 78.4. Hence the free frequencies of two identical bars, one fixed-fixed the other free-free, are alike. As shown in Figs. 78.1A, B, the dynamic deformation curves are dissimilar, by virtue of the different b.c.

Example. Chimes in an orchestra are obtained by striking long cylindrical tubes. Is the sound caused by longitudinal or by transverse vibrations? On physical grounds we should expect the latter to be responsible, because the cylindrical radiating surface for transverse vibrations far exceeds the area of the metal at one end which operates for longitudinal vibrations. We shall now confirm this by calculation for a brass tube 2.5×10^{-2} m. diameter, 10^{-3} m. thick, 1.5 m. long. From §§76, 78,

$$\omega_1 = (k_1 l)^2 (EI/\mathbf{m})^{1/2}/l^2 \qquad 79.1$$

$$= 4.73^2 (I/A_s)^{1/2} (E/\rho)^{1/2}/2.25. \qquad 79.2$$

Now $I = \pi(d_1^4 - d_2^4)/64$, $A_s = \pi(d_1^2 - d_2^2)/4$, d_1, d_2, being the outer and inner diameters, so $(I/A_s)^{1/2} = (d_1^2 + d_2^2)^{1/2}/4 = 8.5 \times 10^{-3}$. Substituting this into 79.2, the frequency of the lowest transverse mode is

$$\omega_1 = 7.61 \times 10^{-2} (E/\rho)^{1/2}. \qquad 79.3$$

For the lowest longitudinal mode, 62.2 gives

$$\omega_1' = (\pi/1.5)(E/\rho)^{1/2}, \qquad 79.4$$

so $$\omega_1'/\omega_1 \simeq 27.6. \qquad 79.5$$

Thus the frequency of the longitudinal is nearly 28 times that of the transverse mode. For brass $c = (E/\rho)^{1/2} \simeq 3.2 \times 10^3$ m.p.sec., so

$$\omega_1 \simeq 240 \quad \text{c.p.s.}, \qquad \text{(transverse)} \qquad 79.6$$

and $$\omega_1' \simeq 6700 \text{ c.p.s.} \qquad \text{(longitudinal)} \qquad 79.7$$

These results and the fact that chimes occur in the middle audio register confirms our physical reasoning above. The overtones are enharmonic, but are relatively innocuous if a soft striker is used.

80. UNIFORM BAR FIXED AT $x = 0$, WITH MASS m AT $x = l$. The b.c. are (i) $\xi = 0$, $x = 0$, (ii) $d\xi/dx = 0$, $x = 0$, (iii) $d^2\xi/dx^2 = 0$, $x = l$, (iv) $d^3\xi/dx^3 = -(\omega^2 m/EI)\xi$, $x = l$ to counteract the accelerational force $-m\partial^2\xi/\partial t^2 = \omega^2 m\xi$, because the shearing force $F = dM/dx = -EId^3\xi/dx^3$, so $d^3\xi/dx^3 = -(\omega^2 m/EI)\xi$ at $x = l$. Using (i)-(iii) in 76.4, yields 77.4. From 77.5, (iv), 76.4, and 78.1

$$A(S - s) + B(C + c)$$
$$= -(\omega^2 m/k^3 EI)\{A(C - c) + B(S - s)\}. \quad 80.1$$

The frequency equation is found by eliminating A, B, between 80.1 and 77.4, which gives

$$\lambda(Cs - Sc)/(1 + Cc) = \beta, \quad\quad 80.2$$

where $\lambda = kl$, $\beta = k^4 EIl/\omega^2 m$ = mass of bar/m. Dividing 80.2 above and below by Cc, gives

$$\lambda(\tan \lambda - \tanh \lambda)/(1 + I/Cc) = \beta. \quad\quad 80.3$$

If $\beta = m_b/m \ll 1$, λ will be small enough for the first four terms in the expansions of the functions in 80.3 to be used, and after reduction, we get

$$\lambda^4\{(1 + 17\lambda^4/105)/(1 + \lambda^4/12)\} = 3\beta, \quad\quad 80.4$$

The first approximation is $\lambda^4 \simeq 3\beta$. Substituting this into $\{\quad\}$, the second approximation is

$$\lambda^4 \simeq 3\beta(1 - 33\beta/140). \quad\quad 80.5$$

Using the values of λ and β from above, leads to

$$\omega_1 \simeq (3EI/ml^3)^{1/2}(1 - 33m_b/280\ m), \quad\quad 80.6$$

as at 13.6, the latter being derived on a kinetic energy basis.

81. FORCED VIBRATION Consider the bar in §77 to be driven at $x = l$ by a transverse force $fe^{i\omega t}$. B.c. (i)-(iii) are as before,

but the shearing force at $x = l$ is now $fe^{i\omega t}$. By 75.1, 75.2, $-EId^3\xi/dx^3 = fe^{i\omega t}$, so condition (iv) is $d^3\xi/dx^3 = -fe^{i\omega t}/EI$ at $x = l$. (i)-(iii) yield 77.4, while by (iv) and 76.4

$$A(S - s) + B(C + c) = -fe^{i\omega t}/k^3EI = -K, \text{ say} \qquad 81.1$$

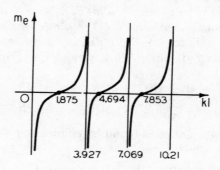

Fig. 81.1.

with $k^4 = \omega^2 m/EI$. Determining A, B, from 77.4, 81.1, and substituting into 77.3, yields

$$\xi(x, t) = \{K/2(1 + Cc)\}\{(S + s)(\cosh kx - \cos kx)$$

$$- (C + c)(\sinh kx - \sin kx)\} \qquad 81.2$$

which is the displacement at x. At $x = l$, 81.2 gives

$$\xi(l, t) = K(Cs - Sc)/(1 + Cc). \qquad 81.3$$

When $(1 + Cc) = 0$, ξ is infinite, and as at 77.7 the natural vibrations of the bar are obtained. When $(Cs - Sc) = 0$, $\xi = 0$ at $x = l$, and the bar vibrates between $x = 0$, l, but *not at* either of these points. The equation is equivalent to

$$\tan kl = \tanh kl, \qquad 81.4$$

whose first four roots are $k_1l \simeq 3.927$, $k_2l \simeq 7.069$, $k_3l \simeq 10.21$, $k_4l \simeq 13.352$. When $kl > 13.352$,

$$\xi(l, t) \simeq K(\tan kl - 1), \qquad 81.5$$

and this vanishes if $\tan kl = 1$, so

$$k_n l \simeq \pi(n + 1/4),$$

$n \geq 5$, and the difference between consecutive roots is nearly π.

Mechanical impedance at driving point. From 81.3, using $e^{i\omega t}$,

$$\xi(l, t) = i\omega K(Cs - Sc)/(1 + Cc). \qquad 81.7$$

Now $fe^{i\omega t}/k^3 EI = kfe^{i\omega t}/\omega^2 \mathbf{m}$, so

$$z = (\text{force/vel.})_{x=l} = -(i\omega \mathbf{m}/k)(1 + Cc)/(Cs - Sc). \qquad 81.8$$

The impedance vanishes when $(1 + Cc) = 0$, i.e. at a natural frequency, and z is infinite if $(Cs - Sc) = 0$, the bar then being stationary at $x = 0, l$, as stated previously. There is no free vibration corresponding to this forced type.

Effective mass. By definition, in absence of loss,

$$m_e = -iz/\omega = -(\mathbf{m}/k)(1 + Cc)/(Cs - Sc). \qquad 81.9$$

Curves showing the relationship between m_e and kl are given in Fig. 81.1.

★82. SOLUTION FOR FORCED VIBRATION BY OPERATIONAL CALCULUS Suppose the bar in §81 is driven by a force $f(x)e^{i\omega t}$

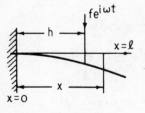

Fig. 82.1A

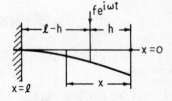

Fig. 82.1B

distributed over its length. The D.E. is 75.4 with an additional term $f(x)e^{i\omega t}$ on the r.h.s. For a uniform bar EI is constant, and we get

$$EI\partial^4\xi/\partial x^4 + \mathbf{m}\partial^2\xi/\partial t^2 = f(x)e^{i\omega t}. \qquad 82.1$$

Substituting $\xi = \xi_1(x)e^{i\omega t}$ gives

$$d^4\xi/dx^4 - k^4\xi = bf(x), \qquad 82.2$$

where $b = 1/EI$, and ξ has been written for ξ_1. With $\xi(x) \Rightarrow \psi(q)$ and $f(x) \Rightarrow \psi_1(q)$, the transform equation for 82.2 is

$$(q^4 - k^4)\psi = b\psi_1 + q^4\xi_0 + q^3\xi_1 + q^2\xi_2 + q\xi_3, \qquad 82.3$$

where $\xi_n = \xi^{(n)}(0)$. The last four terms pertain to the conditions at $x = 0$. In the problem of §81, $\xi_0 = \xi_1 = 0$, but ξ_2, ξ_3 have to be determined from the conditions at $x = l$, i.e. $\xi''(l) = \xi'''(l) = 0$. In [21] the method used below is applied to a hinged bar for various conditions of loading. By virtue of the substitution $\xi = \xi_1(x)e^{i\omega t}$, we assume harmonic motion in $0 \leq x \leq l$. Thus only the forced vibration is obtained. However, the modification (repeated use of L.T.) introduced in §83, permits the derivation of forced and free vibrations. It also enables the former to be obtained immediately in the guise of a Fourier expansion.

We take $f(x) = f$ to be concentrated at some point $x = h$ (Fig. 82.1A) $0 < h < l$, in order to obtain a more general solution than that in §81. Then in accordance with §57, $\psi_1 = fqe^{-qh}$. Thus 82.3 becomes

$$\psi = (bfqe^{-qh} + q^2\xi_2 + q\xi_3)/(q^4 - k^4) \qquad 82.4$$

$$= \{(bfqe^{-qh} + q^2\xi_2 + q\xi_3)/2k^2\}$$
$$\cdot \{1/(q^2 - k^2) - 1/(q^2 + k^2)\}. \qquad 82.5$$

By inversion

$$\xi(x) = (1/2k^3)\{bf[\sinh k(x - h) - \sin k(x - h)]$$
$$+ k\xi_2(\cosh kx - \cos kx) + \xi_3(\sinh kx - \sin kx)\}, \qquad 82.6$$

which applies in the range $h \leq x \leq l$.

Next we find ξ_2, ξ_3 using the conditions at $x = l$. Differentiating 82.6 to get $\xi''(l)$, $\xi'''(l)$, two equations are obtained whose solution gives ξ_2, ξ_3 as follows:

$$k\xi_2 = bf\{(S + s)(Ch + ch)$$

$$- (C + c)(Sh + sh)\}/2(1 + Cc), \qquad 82.7$$

and
$$\xi_3 = bf\{(S + s)(Sh + sh)$$

$$- (C + c)(Ch + ch)\}/2(1 + Cc), \qquad 82.8$$

where C, c, S, s, are as in §77, and $Ch = \cosh k(l - h)$, $ch = \cos k(l - h)$, etc. Inserting 82.7, 82.8 into 82.6 gives the displacement of the bar in $h \leq x \leq l$.

In §81, f is applied at $x = l$, so $h = l$ and then

$$k\xi_2 = bf(S + s)/(1 + Cc) \qquad 82.9$$

$$\xi_3 = -bf(C + c)/(1 + Cc). \qquad 82.10$$

Substituting into 82.6, and restoring the time factor, leads to

$$\xi(x, t) = \{bf/2k^3(1 + Cc)\}\{(S + s)(\cosh kx - \cos kx)$$

$$- (C + c)(\sinh kx - \sin kx)\}e^{i\omega t}, \qquad 82.11$$

which is identical with 81.2.

★*The range* $0 \leq x \leq h$. In §57 we obtained $\xi(x)$ by interchanging the symbols x and h. This is permissible if the (known) b.c. at both ends of the bar are identical. In the above case the b.c. differ at the free and fixed ends, so the analysis needs to be modified. We change the origin as in Fig. 82.1B, so the b.c. are now $\xi'' = \xi''' = 0$, at $x = 0$, and $\xi = \xi' = 0$, at $x = l$. Then in place of 82.4 we get

$$\psi = (bfqe^{-qh} + q^4\xi_0 + q^3\xi_1)/(q^4 - k^4) \qquad 82.12$$

$$= \frac{bfqe^{-qh}}{2k^2}\left\{\frac{1}{q^2 - k^2} - \frac{1}{q^2 + k^2}\right\}$$

$$+ \{(\xi_0 q^2 + \xi_1 q)/2\}\left\{\frac{1}{q^2 - k^2} + \frac{1}{q^2 + k^2}\right\}. \qquad 82.13$$

By inversion

$$\xi(x) = (1/2k^3)\{bf[\sinh k(x - h) - \sin k(x - h)]$$

$$+ k^3\xi_0(\cosh kx + \cos kx) \qquad 82.14$$

$$+ k^2\xi_1(\sinh kx + \sin kx)\}.$$

ξ_0, ξ_1 are now determined by using $\xi = \xi' = 0$, at $x = l$. Finally the symbols may be altered to suit Fig. 82.1A for the range $0 \le x \le h$.

★83. LOAD APPLIED SUDDENLY TO HINGED BAR   In §82, at the outset, we assumed harmonic motion, thereby failing to obtain the natural vibrations, which are incited when a force of any type is applied suddenly at $t = 0$. In practice, where loss occurs, these vibrations are damped out rapidly, although if a harmonic force having a frequency equal to that of one of the natural vibrations is applied, the amplitude may be relatively large. As we have not considered a bar hinged at both ends hitherto, it is opportune to do so now. The method of solution is that used in §58. i.e. repeated L.T. procedure.

The D.E. is 75.4 with $f(x)g(t)^*$ on the r.h.s., so

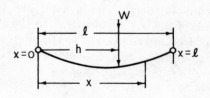

Fig. 83.1

$$\partial^4\xi/\partial x^4 + (m/EI)\partial^2\xi/\partial t^2 = f(x)g(t)/EI, \qquad 83.1$$

$f(x)$ being the distribution of force along the bar, and $g(t)$ the time factor. Taking $\xi(x, t) \Rightarrow \phi(x, p)$, $g(t) \Rightarrow \phi_1(p)$, $b = 1/EI$,

---

*A product function of this type entails a function of t independent of x.

the transform equation for initial quiescence, is [13]

$$d^4\phi/dx^4 - \lambda^4\phi = bf(x)\phi_1(p), \qquad 83.2$$

where $\lambda^4 = -\mathbf{m}p^2/EI$, $\lambda = (iap)^{1/2}$, $a^2 = \mathbf{m}/EI$. To solve 83.1, take $\phi(x, p) \Rightarrow \psi(q, p), f(x) \Rightarrow \psi_1(q)$, and write q for d/dx. Then the transform equation is

$$(q^4 - \lambda^4)\psi = b\phi_1\psi_1 + q^4\phi(0) + q^3\phi'(0) + q^2\phi''(0) + q\phi'''(0), \; 83.3$$

the last four terms pertaining to the conditions at $x = 0$. For a hinged bar, the displacement and bending moment are zero at the supports, so the (known) b.c. are $\xi(0, t) = \xi''(0, t) = 0 = \xi(l, t) = \xi''(l, t)$. Now $\xi(x, t) \Rightarrow \phi(x, p)$, so $\xi(0, t) \Rightarrow \phi(0, p) = 0$, and $\xi''(0, t) \Rightarrow \phi''(0, p) = 0$. Inserting these in 83.3 gives

$$\psi(q, p) = \{b\phi_1\psi_1 + q^3\phi'(0) + q\phi'''(0)\}/(q^4 - \lambda^4). \quad 83.4$$

As in §82, $\phi'(0)$, $\phi'''(0)$ are determined to satisfy the b.c. at $x = l$.

Suppose $f(x)$ is a constant load W^* applied at $x = h$ (Fig. 83.1), when $t = 0$. Then by §82, $\phi_1\psi_1 = Wqe^{-qh}$, so 83.4 becomes

$$\psi(q, p) = \{bWqe^{-qh} + q^3\phi'(0) + q\phi'''(0)\}/(q^4 - \lambda^4), \quad 83.5$$

and by 82.4, 82.6, 82.12, 82.14

$$\phi = (1/2\lambda^3)\{bW[\sinh \lambda(x - h) - \sin \lambda(x - h)]$$
$$+ \lambda^2\phi'(0)[\sinh \lambda x + \sin \lambda x] \qquad 83.6$$
$$+ \phi'''(0)[\sinh \lambda x - \sin \lambda x]\}.$$

Using 83.6 and the b.c. at $x = l$, we find that

$$\lambda^2\phi'(0) = (bW/2)\left\{\frac{\sin \lambda(l - h)}{\sin \lambda l} - \frac{\sinh \lambda(l - h)}{\sinh \lambda l}\right\}, \quad 83.7$$

and $\quad \phi'''(0) = -(bW/2)\left\{\frac{\sin \lambda(l - h)}{\sin \lambda l} + \frac{\sinh \lambda(l - h)}{\sinh \lambda l}\right\}. \quad 83.8$

---

*This is equivalent to $WH(t)$, so $g(t) = H(t) \Rightarrow \phi_1 = 1$—see §30.

Inserting these into 83.6 leads to the solution of 83.2, namely,

$$\phi(x, p) = (bW/2\lambda^3)\Big\{[\sinh \lambda(x - h) - \sin \lambda(x - h)]$$

$$+ \Big[\frac{\sin \lambda x \sin \lambda(l - h)}{\sin \lambda l} - \frac{\sinh \lambda x \sinh \lambda(l - h)}{\sinh \lambda l}\Big]\Big\}, \qquad 83.9$$

for the interval $h \leq x \leq l$.

Taking $\lambda = (iaz)^{1/2}$, application of the Mellin theorem [12] gives

$$\xi(x, t) = \frac{(bW/2)}{2\pi i} \int_{c-i\infty}^{c+i\infty} e^{zt}\{\text{as at 83.9}\} \, dz/\lambda^3 z. \qquad 83.10$$

The singularities of the integrand in 83.10 are all simple poles,* and the value of the integral is the sum of the residues thereat.
(a) The only singularity of

$$e^{zt}\{\sinh \lambda(x - h) - \sin \lambda(x - h)\}/\lambda^3 z \qquad 83.11$$

is a simple pole at $z = 0$. Expanding sinh, sin, and using the first two terms of each series when z is small, yields

$$e^{zt}\lambda^3(x - h)^3/3\lambda^3 z = e^{zt}(x - h)^3/3z, \text{ so}$$

the residue at $z = 0$ is

$$(x - h)^3/3. \qquad 83.12$$

(b) $e^{zt}\Big\{\dfrac{\sin \lambda x \sin \lambda(l - h)}{\lambda^3 z \sin \lambda l} - \dfrac{\sinh \lambda x \sinh \lambda(l - h)}{\lambda^3 z \sinh \lambda l}\Big\}, \qquad$ 83.13

has a simple pole at $z = 0$. Taking the first two terms of each expansion, with an obvious notation, we obtain

$$(\alpha\beta/\gamma\lambda^3 z)\Big\{\frac{(1 - \alpha^2/6)(1 - \beta^2/6)}{(1 - \gamma^2/6)}$$

$$- \frac{(1 + \alpha^2/6)(1 + \beta^2/6)}{(1 + \gamma^2/6)}\Big\}e^{zt} \qquad 83.14$$

---

*See below 66.5 regarding limit point for the poles as $z \to \infty$.

$$= x(l - h)(2lh - h^2 - x^2)e^{zt}/3lz, \qquad 83.15$$

after reduction and restoration of the original symbols. Thus the residue at $z = 0$, is

$$x(l - h)(2lh - h^2 - x^2)/3l. \qquad 83.16$$

Adding 83.12 and 83.16, and using the external multiplier from 83.10, yields

$$Wh(l - x)(2lx - x^2 - h^2)/6EIl, \qquad 83.17$$

which is the statical deflection of the bar in the interval $h \leq x \leq l$. For the interval $0 \leq x \leq h$, interchange x and h, this being valid since the (known) b.c. at $x = 0$, l are identical.

(c) The poles of the first fraction in 83.13, other than $z = 0$, occur when $\sin \lambda l = 0$, so $\lambda = n\pi/l$, $\pm n = 1, 2, \cdots$. Then remembering that $\lambda = (iaz)^{1/2}$, $\lambda^4 = -a^2z^2$,

$\sum$ residues

$$= \sum_{n=1}^{\infty} \left\{ \frac{e^{zt} \sin \lambda x \sin \lambda(l - h)}{\lambda^3 z \, d(\sin \lambda l)/dz} \right\}_{\lambda \to n\pi l} \qquad 83.18$$

$$= 2 \sum_{n=1}^{\infty} \left\{ \frac{e^{zt} \sin \lambda x \sin \lambda(l - h)}{l\lambda^4 \cos \lambda l} \right\}_{z=-in^2\pi^2/al^2} \qquad 83.19$$

$$= -2(l^3/\pi^4) \sum_{n=1}^{\infty} (1/n)^4 e^{-in^2\pi^2t/al^2} \sin(n\pi x/l) \sin(n\pi h/l). \qquad 83.20$$

(d) The poles of the second fraction in 83.13, apart from $z = 0$, occur when $\sinh \lambda l = 0$, so $\lambda = in\pi/l$, $\pm n = 1, 2, \cdots$. Proceeding as above we obtain

$$\sum \text{ residues} = \text{as at 83.20 but with } i \text{ for } -i. \qquad 83.21$$

Adding the residues in 83.20, 83.21 and using the external multiplier from 83.10, leads to the expression for the natural vibrations, namely,

$$-2(Wl^3/\pi^4EI) \sum_{n=1}^{\infty} (1/n)^4 \sin(n\pi x/l)$$

$$83.22$$

124

$$\sin (n\pi h/l) \cos (n^2\pi^2 t/al^2),$$

in $h \leq x \leq l$. For the interval $0 \leq x \leq h$, interchanging x and h leaves 83.22 unaltered, as we should expect on physical grounds. The complete result is the sum of 83.17 and 83.22.

The infinite frequency spectrum of the suddenly applied load W is converted into a line spectrum whose frequencies are the natural modes of the bar, together with a line at zero frequency due to the static deflection. Apart from the latter, the only line of importance is that for the fundamental $\omega_1 = \pi^2/al^2$, because the amplitudes of the overtones fall off as $1/n^4$. It should be noticed that the overtones are harmonic, whereas for other end conditions they are enharmonic.

If W is applied at the centre of the bar, $\sin n\pi h/l = \sin n\pi/2 = (-1)^{n-1}$ when n is odd, but zero when even. Hence only odd harmonics occur,[*] since the mid-point is nodal for the even ones (see §53).

If $g(t)$ varies with time, instead of being constant as above, the integrand of 83.10 must be multiplied by $\phi_1(z)$ before evaluation. For instance let $g(t) = \sin \omega t \rightleftharpoons \omega p/(p^2 + \omega^2)$, then there are additional simple poles at $z = \pm i\omega$, $\omega \neq \omega_n$, a natural frequency.[**] The ω_n are derived from the poles of the new integrand, so their amplitudes depend upon $g(t)$, but their frequencies are unchanged. In 83.22 the amplitudes are as $1/n^4$, whereas for $g(t) = \sin \omega t$ the ratio is $1/\{n^6\pi^4(1 - a^2\omega^2 l^4/n^6\pi^4)\}$, provided that $\omega \neq n^2\pi^2/al^2 = \omega_n$.

If an impulse $SI(t)$, as in §29, is applied at $x = h$, $t = 0$, the resulting displacement may be obtained from 83.17 + 83.22 by differentiating with respect to t, and replacement of W by S. This follows from the fact that $SI(t) \rightleftharpoons Sp$, and $f'(t) \rightleftharpoons p\phi(p)$, if $f(0) = 0$. The differentiation with respect to t is valid since 83.22 is *uniformly* convergent in $0 \leq t_1 \leq t$, as also is the derived series. Hence for $SI(t)$ we get

---

[*] $\omega_n = n^2\pi^2/al^2$, so the frequency ratios to that of the fundamental are 9, 25, 49, $\cdots$

[**] See footnote to text below 58.10.

$$\xi(x,\ t) = (2Sal^2/\pi^2 m_b) \sum_{n=1}^{\infty} (1/n)^2 \sin\ (n\pi x/l)$$

82.23

$$\sin\ (n\pi h/l) \sin\ (n^2\pi^2 t/al^2),$$

where m_b is the mass of the whole bar. 83.23 shows that the amplitude ratio of the harmonics is now $1/n^2$ instead of $1/n^4$ as in 83.21, which exemplifies the influence of forces having different frequency spectra. The spectrum of W is that of unit function $H(t)$,† i.e. $1/\omega$, which $\rightarrow 0$ as $\omega \rightarrow +\infty$, whereas that of $SI(t)$ is uniform.

83.22 is valid at $t = 0$, by virtue of *uniform* convergence. Since $\xi(x, 0) = 0$, it follows from 83.17 and 83.22, that

$$h(l - x)(2lx - x^2 - h^2)$$

83.24

$$= 12(l/\pi)^4 \sum_{n=1}^{\infty} (1/n)^4 \sin\ (n\pi x/l) \sin\ (n\pi h/l)$$

in $h \leq x \leq l$, and by interchange of x, h,

$$x(l - h)(2lh - h^2 - x^2) = \text{as at r.h.s. of 83.24} \qquad 83.25$$

in $0 \leq x \leq h$. The r.h.s. of 83.24, 83.25 represent the Fourier expansions of the statical displacement, for unit load, in the respective ranges of x.

★84. FREE VIBRATIONS OF WEDGE CLAMPED AT BASE (FIG. 84.1). The D.E. is 75.4, with $I = b(ax/l)^3/12$, $\mathbf{m} = \rho abx/l$,

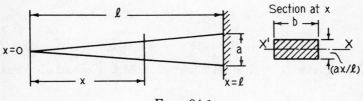

FIG. 84.1

$\partial^2 \xi / \partial t^2 = -\omega^2 \xi$ for harmonic motion in a particular mode of vibration. Thus writing ξ for $\xi(x)$,

$$(Eba^3/12l^3)\frac{d^2}{dx^2}\left(x^3\frac{d^2\xi}{dx^2}\right) = (\rho ab\omega^2/l)x\xi, \qquad 84.1$$

so

$$\frac{d^2}{dx^2}\left(x^3\frac{d^2\xi}{dx^2}\right) - k^4 x\xi = 0, \qquad 84.2$$

where $k^4 = (12\omega^2 l^2/a^2)(\rho/E)$, having dimension l^{-2}. From 84.2 we get

$$x^3\xi^{iv} + 6x^2\xi''' + 6x\xi'' - k^4 x\xi = 0, \qquad 84.3$$

or

$$x^2\xi^{iv} + 6x\xi''' + 6\xi'' - k^4\xi = 0. \qquad 84.4$$

Assume that 84.4 may be expressed in the form

$$(xd^2/dx^2 + \alpha d/dx + k^2)(xd^2/dx^2 + \beta d/dx - k^2)\xi = 0, \qquad 84.5$$

the bracketed expressions being permutable linear operators. Performing the operations indicated, yields

$$\left.\begin{array}{l} k^2\{x\xi'' + \beta\xi' - k^2\xi\} \\[2mm] \alpha\{x\xi''' + (\beta + 1)\xi'' - k^2\xi'\}, \\[2mm] x\{x\xi^{iv} + (\beta + 2)\xi''' - k^2\xi''\}. \end{array}\right\} \qquad 84.6$$

and

By addition

$$x^2\xi^{iv} + (\alpha + \beta + 2)x\xi''' + \alpha(\beta + 1)\xi''$$
$$\qquad\qquad + (\beta - \alpha)k^2\xi' - k^4\xi = 0. \qquad 84.7$$

Taking $\alpha = \beta = 2$ in 84.7, equation 84.4 is obtained. Thus from 84.5

$$(xd^2/dx^2 + 2d/dx + k^2)(xd^2/dx^2 + 2d/dx - k^2)\xi = 0, \qquad 84.8$$

and by the theory of linear D.E. the solution of 84.4 is the sum of the solutions of

$$x\xi'' + 2\xi' + k^2\xi = 0, \quad \text{and} \quad x\xi'' + 2\xi' - k^2\xi = 0. \quad 84.9$$

Substituting $\xi = yx^{-1/2}$ and then $z = x^{1/2}$ in the first equation, leads to

$$d^2y/dz^2 + (1/z)\,dy/dz + (4k^2 - 1/z^2)y = 0. \quad 84.10$$

This is the standard form of Bessel's equation, whose complete solution with two arbitrary constants, is

$$y = AJ_1(2kz) + BY_1(2kz). \quad 84.11$$

Using the same substitutions as above, the second equation in 84.9 transforms to the modified Bessel equation

$$d^2y/dz^2 + (1/z)\,dy/dz - (4k^2 + 1/z^2)y = 0, \quad 84.12$$

whose complete solution is

$$y = CI_1(2kz) + DK_1(2kz). \quad 84.13$$

Restoring the original variables in 84.11, 84.13, and adding the resulting expressions, yields the complete formal solution of 84.4, namely,

$$\xi(x) = x^{-1/2}\{AJ_1(2kx^{1/2}) + BY_1(2kx^{1/2})$$
$$\qquad\qquad\qquad\qquad 84.14$$
$$+ CI_1(2kx^{1/2}) + DK_1(2kx^{1/2})\}.$$

★*Vibrational frequencies.* The b.c. are (i) $\xi = 0$, $x = l$, (ii) $d\xi/dx = 0$, $x = l$, these two referring to displacement and slope of the axis; (iii) $d^2\xi/dx^2 = 0$, $x = 0$, i.e. zero bending moment at the tip, (iv) $d(EId^2\xi/dx^2)/dx = 0$, $x = 0$, i.e. zero shear, so $d(x^3d^2\xi/dx^2)/dx = x^3d^3\xi/dx^3 + 3x^2d^2\xi/dx^2 = 0$. Now it may be shown that in virtue of the singularities of Y_1 and K_1 at $x = 0$, they are inadmissible solutions, except when the tip of the bar is removed, so we must have $B = D = 0$. Then 84.14 becomes

$$\xi = x^{-1/2}\{AJ_1(2kx^{1/2}) + CI_1(2kx^{1/2})\}, \quad 84.15$$

and (i) gives

$$AJ_1(2kl^{1/2}) + CI_1(2kl^{1/2}) = 0. \quad 84.16$$

To differentiate ξ in 84.15, we use the formulae [11]

$$d\{u^{-1}J_1(u)\}/dx = -u^{-1}J_2(u)\ du/dx,$$

$$d\{u^{-1}I_1(u)\}/dx = u^{-1}I_2(u)\ du/dx,$$

84.17

thereby obtaining

$$d\xi/dx = -kx^{-1}\{AJ_2(2kx^{1/2}) - CI_2(2kx^{1/2})\}. \qquad 84.18$$

Using b.c. (ii) gives

$$AJ_2(2kl^{1/2}) - CI_2(2kl^{1/2}) = 0. \qquad 84.19$$

Eliminating A, C between 84.16, 84.19 yields the frequency equation

$$J_1(\lambda)I_2(\lambda) + J_2(\lambda)I_1(\lambda) = 0, \qquad 84.20$$

with $\lambda = 2kl^{1/2}$. The first root of 84.20 is $2k_1l^{1/2} \simeq 4.612$, and those of higher rank are 7.799, 10.958, 14.109, 17.256, $\cdots$. Others may be calculated from the formula [1]

$$\lambda_m = 2k_ml^{1/2} \simeq \theta - (3/8\theta)\{1 + (1/\theta)$$

$$+ (15/16\theta^2) + (9/8\theta^3) + \cdots\},$$

84.21

where $\theta = (2m + 1)\pi/2$, $m \geq 2$ being the rank of the root. As m increases $(\lambda_{m+1} - \lambda_m) \to \pi$. Since $k^4 = (12\omega^2l^2/a^2)(\rho/E)$, we obtain

$$\omega_m = (\lambda_m^2 a/8\ \sqrt{3}\ l^2)(E/\rho)^{1/2}, \qquad 84.22$$

which is independent of the breadth of the bar. The overtones are enharmonic, the ratios of their frequencies to that of the fundamental being: 2.86, 5.70, 9.48, 14.02, $\cdots$, approximately. From 84.22 and 77.10, the ratio of the fundamental frequency of a wedge shaped bar and the corresponding rectangular bar of basal thickness a, is

$$\lambda_1^2/4(k_1l)^2 \simeq 4.612^2/4 \times 1.875^2 \simeq 1.51. \qquad 84.23$$

We have used b.c. (i), (ii) only, but by aid of 84.15 it may be shown that (iii), (iv) are satisfied also, which is left for the reader to verify.

CHAPTER VIII

Vibration of Circular and Annular Membranes

85. SYMMETRICAL VIBRATION OF CIRCULAR MEMBRANE If a very thin piece of aluminium foil, say 2×10^{-5} m. thick, is stretched to a uniform tension over a circular frame and clamped in position, it constitutes a membrane which vibrates when tapped. Theoretically a membrane has flexibility but not stiffness, and although this cannot be realised in practice, the aluminium foil is a good approximation. Using hypotheses (a)-(e) in §50, we shall derive the D.E. for those vibrations which

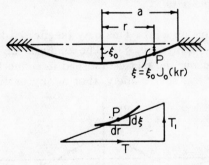

$$\xi = \xi_0 J_0(kr)$$

Fig. 85.1

entail a dynamic deformation surface of revolution about the axis. Referring to Fig. 85.1, T is the total tension or pull on a circle of radius r, while T_1 is the vertical component thereof. By similar triangles

$$T_1/T = -\partial\xi/\partial r, \qquad \text{or} \qquad T_1 = -T\partial\xi/\partial r, \qquad 85.1$$

the minus sign signifying decrease in ξ with increase in r. If **T** is the uniform tension per *unit* of circumference at $r = a$, then at radius $r < a$, $T = 2\pi r\mathbf{T}$, so

$$T_1 = -2\pi Tr\partial\xi/\partial r, \qquad\qquad 85.2$$

and $$\partial T_1/\partial r = -2\pi T\{r\partial^2\xi/\partial r^2 + \partial\xi/\partial r\}. \qquad 85.3$$

The net force on an annulus of width dr, is the difference in the vertical forces at its edges, namely,

$$\partial T_1 = -2\pi Tr\, dr\{\partial^2\xi/\partial r^2 + \partial\xi/r\partial r\}. \qquad 85.4$$

Since the membrane vibrates freely, the sum of the elastic and inertia forces must vanish. The latter is

$$\text{mass of annulus} \times \partial^2\xi/\partial t^2 = 2\pi r\mathbf{m}\, dr(\partial^2\xi/\partial t^2). \qquad 85.5$$

Adding the r.h.s. of 85.4, 85.5, gives

$$\partial^2\xi/\partial r^2 + \partial\xi/r\partial r - c^2\partial^2\xi/\partial t^2 = 0, \qquad 85.6$$

where $c^2 = \mathbf{m}/\mathbf{T}$, $\mathbf{m}$ the mass per unit area of the membrane of uniform thickness.

86. SOLUTION OF 85.6 This may be effected by the separation method employed in §51. The analysis can be shortened, however, by using the fact established in connection with continuous linear systems, namely, that in any particular mode of

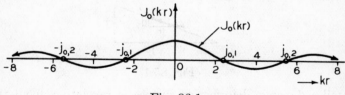

Fig. 86.1

vibration, the motion is harmonic. Thus we write $\xi(r, t) = \xi_1(r)e^{i\omega t}$, which gives $\partial^2\xi/\partial t^2 = -\omega^2\xi_1 e^{i\omega t}$, ω being the frequency of the mode. Substituting into 85.6 yields the ordinary D.E.

$$d^2\xi_1/dr^2 + d\xi_1/r\, dr + k^2\xi_1 = 0, \qquad 86.1$$

where $k = \omega/c$. This is a Bessel equation whose complete solution, with two arbitrary constants, is

$$\xi_1(r) = A J_0(kr) + B Y_0(kr), \qquad 86.2$$

so $\qquad \xi(r, t) = \{A J_0(kr) + B Y_0(kr)\}e^{i\omega t}. \qquad 86.3$

The b.c. are (i) $\xi_1 = \xi_0$, $r = 0$, (ii) $\xi_1 = 0$, $r = a$ at the clamp. The first condition signifies that during vibration the central amplitude has been assigned the arbitrary value ξ_0. At the centre where $r = 0$, $Y_0(kr)$ is undefined by virtue of its singularity, and ceases to be a solution.* Hence $B = 0$. Now $J_0(0) = 1$, so (i) gives $A = \xi_0$, and the appropriate solution is

$$\xi_1(r) = \xi_0 J_0(kr), \qquad \xi(r, t) = \xi_0 J_0(kr)e^{i\omega t}, \qquad 86.4$$

where the real part is chosen. From (ii) and 86.4, we get the frequency equation

$$J_0(ka) = 0. \qquad 86.5$$

Accordingly ka must always be such that 86.5 is satisfied, i.e. it must be a zero of the Bessel function, whose graph is given in Fig. 86.1. There is an infinity of positive zeros which occur when $ka \simeq 2.405$, 5.52, 8.654, 11.792, and so on. The negative zeros occur at $ka \simeq -2.405$, etc., but they are not needed here. We shall use the symbol $j_{0,m}$ to signify a zero, 0 being the order of the Bessel function, and m the rank of the zero, e.g. $j_{0,2} \simeq 5.52$. Thus $k_m a = j_{0,m}$, so $k_m = j_{0,m}/a$, and since $k_m = \omega_m/c$, we get

$$\omega_m = (j_{0,m}/a)(\mathbf{T}/\mathbf{m})^{1/2}. \qquad 86.6$$

Example. If aluminium foil 2×10^{-5} m. thick, $\rho = 2.7 \times 10^3$ kg. per m.^{3} is stretched over a metal framework 2×10^{-2} m. radius, the radial tension per unit length of periphery being 5.4×10^3 newton,**what are the frequencies of the symmetrical modes?

---

*$Y_0(kr)$ must be retained for an annular membrane, as in §89, because $r > 0$.

**A newton is 10^5 dynes.

By 86.6

$$\omega_1 = (2.405/2 \times 10^{-2})(5.4 \times 10^3/5.4 \times 10^{-2})^{1/2}$$

$$\simeq 3.8 \times 10^4, \tag{86.7}$$

so $\omega_1/2\pi \simeq 6000$ c.p.s. *in vacuo*. $\tag{86.8}$

The frequency of the mth mode is $6000 \times j_{0,m}/j_{0,1} \simeq 2500$ $j_{0,m}$. Thus for $m = 3$, $\omega_3/2\pi \simeq 2500 \times 8.654 \simeq 21640$ c.p.s. The frequencies for vibration in air would be less than these (see §50 and ref. [10]), by virtue of 'accession to inertia'. Also the dynamic deformation curve would differ from that discussed in §87. It should be noticed that the overtones *in vacuo* are not integral multiples of the fundamental, so they are enharmonic. This is due to the variation in mass per unit radius, for $dm/dr = 2\pi r \mathbf{m}$.

87. DYNAMIC DEFORMATION CURVE When vibrating in its fundamental mode, the whole membrane moves in the same direction at any instant. The d.d.c. is an axial section, its shape being that of $J_0(kr)$ in Fig. 86.1 from $kr = -2.405$ to $+2.405$, such that when $r = 0$, $\xi = \xi_0 \cos \omega_1 t$. For the second mode $J_0(\pm 5.52) = 0$, and the shape is that in Fig. 86.1 from $kr = -5.52$ to $+5.52$. Thus when $kr = 2.405$ there is a nodal circle of radius $r = 2.405/k_2 = 2.405a/5.52 \simeq 0.436a$. In general for the mth mode, there are $(m - 1)$ nodal circles *within* the clamps.

★88. EQUIVALENT MASS IN FUNDAMENTAL MODE This is defined to be the rigid mass, which vibrating with the central velocity, has the same K.E. as the whole membrane.† The mass of an annular ring of width dr and radius r is $2\pi \mathbf{m} r\, dr$, and by 86.4 the max. velocity is $\omega\xi_{max} = \omega\xi_0 J_0(kr)$. Thus the K.E. for the whole membrane is

---

†This differs from 'effective' mass, which applies only to a driven membrane.

$$\pi\mathbf{m}\omega^2\xi_0^2 \int_0^a rJ_0^2(kr) \, dr = (\omega^2\xi_0^2/2)(\pi a^2\mathbf{m})[J_0^2(ka) + J_1^2(ka)]. \qquad 88.1$$

For the fundamental mode, $ka \simeq 2.405$, $J_0(ka) = 0$, $J_1(ka) \simeq 0.52$, so $J_1^2(2.405) \simeq 0.27$, and the equivalent mass is

$$m_q \simeq 0.27 \text{ natural mass.} \qquad 88.2$$

89. ANNULAR MEMBRANE Here we suppose that the membrane is clamped at $r = a$, $r = b$, $0 < b < a$. The b.c. are (i) $\xi = 0$, $r = a$, (ii) $\xi = 0$, $r = b$. Inserting these into 86.2 gives

$$AJ_0(ka) + BY_0(ka) = 0, \text{ and } AJ_0(kb) + BY_0(kb) = 0. \qquad 89.1$$

Equating the values of A/B in 89.1 yields the frequency equation

$$J_0(ka)Y_0(kb) - J_0(kb)Y_0(ka) = 0. \qquad 89.2$$

If $\varphi y = ka$, $y = kb$, the mth root of 89.2 is

$$y = x + (p/x) + (q - p^2)/x^3$$
$$\qquad\qquad + (s - 4pq + 2p^3)/x^5 + \cdots, \qquad 89.3$$

where

$$x = m\pi/\varphi - 1), \; p = -1/8\varphi,$$
$$q = 100(\varphi^3 - 1)/3(8\varphi)^3(\varphi - 1),$$
$$s = -34336(\varphi^5 - 1)/5(8\varphi)^5(\varphi - 1),$$

$m = 1, 2, 3, \cdots$, $\varphi = a/b$. Taking $a = 2 \times 10^{-2}$ m. $b = 10^{-2}$ m., $\lambda\varphi = 2$, with $m = 1$,

$$y = kb = \pi - (1/16\pi) + 163/3072\pi^3 + \cdots \qquad 89.4$$

$$\simeq 3.12, \qquad \text{so} \qquad k_1 \simeq 3.12 \times 10^2. \qquad 89.5$$

Since $k_1 = \omega_1(\mathbf{m/T})^{1/2}$, using the data in §86,

$$\omega_1 \simeq 3.12 \times 10^{9/2} \simeq 9.86 \times 10^4, \qquad 89.6$$

and $\qquad \omega_1/2\pi \simeq 15700$ c.p.s. $\qquad\qquad\qquad 89.7$

Thus fixation of the central part of the membrane raises its fundamental frequency a little more than 2.6 times.

When x in 89.3 is large enough, i.e. $\varphi = a/b$ is near unity, $y \simeq m\pi/(\varphi - 1)$, since this term dominates. The frequency ratios then follow the sequence of the natural numbers. In the above example, the higher frequencies are nearly 2, 3, 4, $\cdots$, times that at 89.7.

90. ANNULAR MEMBRANE DRIVEN AT INNER RADIUS   The b.c. are (i) $\xi = 0$, $r = a$, (ii) by 85.2, $fe^{i\omega t} = -2\pi\mathbf{T}(r\partial\xi/\partial r)_{r=b}$, so $(\partial\xi_1/\partial r)_{r=b} = -f/2\pi\mathbf{T}b$. By (i) and 86.2

$$A J_0(ka) + B Y_0(ka) = 0. \qquad 90.1$$

Now $dJ_0(kr)/dr = -kJ_1(kr)$, $dY_0(kr)/dr = -kY_1(kr)$, so by (ii) and 86.2,

$$A J_1(kb) + B Y_1(kb) = f/2\pi\mathbf{T}kb. \qquad 90.2$$

Solving these equations for A, B, and substituting into 86.3, yields

$$\xi(r, t) = (f/2\pi\mathbf{T}kb)\left\{\frac{J_0(ka) Y_0(kr) - J_0(kr) Y_0(ka)}{J_0(ka) Y_1(kb) - J_1(kb) Y_0(ka)}\right\}e^{i\omega t}. \qquad 90.3$$

Mechanical impedance. At $r = b$ the input impedance is $fe^{i\omega t}/\xi(b, t)$, so [10]

$$z = -i(2\pi b\omega\mathbf{m}/k)\left\{\frac{J_0(ka) Y_1(kb) - J_1(kb) Y_0(ka)}{J_0(ka) Y_0(kb) - J_0(kb) Y_0(ka)}\right\}, \qquad 90.4$$

and the effective mass is $m_e = -iz/\omega$. The form of the m_e-ω curves is similar to those in Fig. 55.1. When ka, kb are large enough for the dominant terms in the asymptotic expansions of the Bessel functions to be used [11], 90.4 simplifies to

$$z = -i(2\pi b\omega\mathbf{m}/k) \cot k(a - b), \qquad 90.5$$

so $\qquad\qquad m_e = -(2\pi b\mathbf{m}/k) \cot k(a - b). \qquad 90.6$

It follows that since $k(a - b) = \omega(a - b)/c$, the m_e-ω curves are ultimately of the cotangent variety. Asymptotes occur when the denominator of 90.4 vanishes, and m_l is then infinitely discontinuous (under the hypothesis in §50). This corresponds to a natural symmetrical mode of the annulus, for at the inner radius b, there is absence of motion, and the frequency equation is 89.2, i.e. zero denominator as above. When the numerator of 90.4 vanishes, z and m_a do likewise, and a resonant condition occurs, the amplitude at b being infinite (in theory!).

★91. GENERAL CASE The partial D.E. in cartesian coordinates is [19]

$$\partial^2\xi/\partial x^2 + \partial^2\xi/\partial y^2 - (1/c^2)\partial^2\xi/\partial t^2 = 0. \qquad 91.1$$

Expressing this in polar coordinates, with $\xi = \xi_1 e^{i\omega t}$, $\xi_1 = \chi(r)\psi(\theta)$, where $\chi(r)$ is a function of r alone, and $\psi(\theta)$ one of θ alone, leads to the D.E.

$$r^2\partial^2\xi/\partial r^2 + r\partial\xi/\partial r + \partial^2\xi/\partial\theta^2 + k^2r^2\xi = 0, \qquad 91.2$$

where ξ has been written for ξ_1 to avoid confusion later.

Substituting $\xi = \chi\psi$ and proceeding as in §51, yields the two ordinary equations

$$d^2\chi/dr^2 + d\chi/r\,dr + (k^2 - \nu^2/r^2)\chi = 0, \qquad 91.3$$

and

$$d^2\psi/d\theta^2 + \nu^2\psi = 0, \qquad 91.4$$

where ν^2 is the separation constant. The respective solutions of these D.E. are

$$\chi_\nu = A_\nu J_\nu(kr) + B_\nu Y_\nu(kr), \qquad 91.5$$

and

$$\psi_\nu = C_\nu \cos\nu\theta + D_\nu \sin\nu\theta. \qquad 91.6$$

In passing round a circle radius r on the membrane at any instant, ξ in general varies with θ. The variation in ξ must be repeated after $\theta = 2\pi$, but may be repeated at a submultiple thereof. Hence ν must be a positive integer n, and the formal solution of 91.2 of order n, is

$$\xi_n(r, \theta) = \{A_nJ_n(kr) + B_nY_n(kr)\}\{C_n \cos n\theta + D_n \sin n\theta\}, \quad 91.7$$

the time factor being omitted, but tacitly understood to be present.

By virtue of the singularity of $Y_n(kr)$ at $r = 0$, this part of the solution is inadmissible for a membrane complete to the centre, but must be retained for an annulus. Thus for the circle, $B = 0$, and

$$\xi_n(r, \theta) = J_n(kr)\{C_n \cos n\theta + D_n \sin n\theta\}, \quad 91.8$$

A_n being absorbed in C_n, D_n. The bracketed expression may be written $(C_n^2 + D_n^2)^{1/2} \cos (n\theta - \epsilon_n)$, where $\epsilon_n = \tan^{-1}D_n/C_n$, so 91.8 becomes

$$\xi_n(r, \theta) = A_nJ_n(kr) \cos (n\theta - \epsilon_n), \quad 91.9$$

with $A_n = (C_n^2 + D_n^2)^{1/2}$, usually differing from the value in 91.7.

★92. VIBRATIONAL MODES At the peripheral clamp $\xi_n(a, \theta) = 0$, so either

$$J_n(ka) = 0, \quad \text{or} \quad \cos (n\theta - \epsilon_n) = 0, \quad 92.1$$

the former being the frequency equation. For every $n = 0, 1, 2, \cdots$, $J_n(ka)$ has an infinity of roots which we designate by $k_{n,m} a = j_{n,m}$, $m = 1, 2, \cdots$, being the rank of the root. A short table, correct to 3 d.p., is given below.

TABLE OF ROOTS OF $J_n(ka) = 0$.

m	$n = 0$	$n = 1$	$n = 2$	$n = 3$	$n = 4$
1	2.405	3.832	5.135	6.379	7.586
2	5.520	7.016	8.417	9.760	11.064
3	8.654	10.173	11.620	13.017	14.373
4	11.792	13.323	14.796	16.224	17.616

Each value of $j_{n,m}$ corresponds to a vibrational mode, and all of them have different frequencies, because the zeros of the

Bessel functions of order n are interlaced. Since the ranges of n, m are infinite, there is a double infinity of modes. During

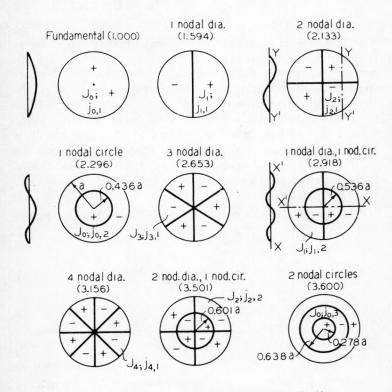

The numbers in ( ) are the frequency ratios to the fundamental for a membrane.

Fig. 92.1

vibration in any *symmetrical* mode, an axial cross-section of the membrane is given (to scale) by $J_0(kr)$ from $kr = -j_{0,m}$ to $+j_{0,m}$. From the shape of $J_0(kr)$, it follows that $(m - 1)$ nodal circles occur within the clamps.

In 91.9, ϵ_n is merely a phase angle, so $\xi_n(r, \theta) = 0$, if we take $\epsilon_n = 0$, and put

$$\cos n\theta = 0, \qquad \text{i.e. } \theta = (2m - 1)\pi/2n. \qquad 92.2$$

With $m = 1, 2, \cdots, \theta = \pi/2n, 3\pi/2n, 5\pi/2n, \cdots$. Taking $n = 1, \theta = \pi/2, 3\pi/2$, and the remainder merely repeat these. Hence the vertical diameter of the membrane is nodal. In general n gives the number of nodal diameters, and they are spaced at equal angular intervals. Moreover, the order of the Bessel function indicates the number of nodal diameters, while the rank of the root less 1, gives the number of nodal circles. Some nodal patterns are depicted in Fig. 92.1, and it will be seen that as $k_{n,m}a = j_{n,m}$ increases (rise in frequency), the pattern may be nodal diameters, nodal circles,* or a mixture of both, according to the values of n, m.

---

*The function of order zero is the only one which yields purely symmetrical modes, since $n \geq 1$ entails this number of nodal diameters.

CHAPTER IX

Transverse Vibration of Circular Plate

93. THE D.E. With assumptions (a)-(e) in §50 and others given in texts on elasticity, the D.E. for a thin plate, expressed in cartesian coordinates, is [19, 20]

$$\partial^4\xi/\partial x^4 + \partial^4\xi/\partial y^4 + 2\partial^4\xi/\partial x^2\partial y^2 + (1/c^2)\partial^2\xi/\partial t^2 = 0, \qquad 93.1$$

where $c^2 = Eh^2/12\rho(1 - \sigma^2) =$ (flexural rigidity)$/\rho h^2$, having dimensions $l^4 t^{-2} =$ (length $\times$ velocity)^2, $\sigma =$ Poisson's ratio <1, $h =$ uniform thickness. The motion in any mode being harmonic, we put $\xi(x, y, t) = \xi_1(x, y)e^{i\omega t}$ and 93.1 becomes

$$\partial^4\xi/\partial x^4 + \partial^4\xi/\partial y^4 + 2\partial^4\xi/\partial x^2\partial y^2 - k^4\xi = 0, \qquad 93.2$$

ξ replacing ξ_1, and $k^4 = (\omega/c)^2$, k having dimension l^{-1}. Following the procedure in §84, we express 93.2 in terms of linear permutable operators, and obtain

$$\left(\frac{\partial^2}{\partial x^2} + \frac{\partial^2}{\partial y^2} + k^2\right)\left(\frac{\partial^2}{\partial x^2} + \frac{\partial^2}{\partial y^2} - k^2\right)\xi = 0. \qquad 93.3$$

Then the solution of 93.2 is the sum of the solutions of the linear D.E.

$$\partial^2\xi/\partial x^2 + \partial^2\xi/\partial y^2 \pm k^2\xi = 0. \qquad 93.4$$

94. TRANSFORMATION OF 93.4 TO POLAR COORDINATES This being expedient in dealing with a *circular* plate, by established procedure we obtain the two partial D.E.

$$r^2\partial^2\xi/\partial r^2 + r\partial\xi/\partial r + \partial^2\xi/\partial\theta^2 \pm k^2 r^2\xi = 0. \qquad 94.1$$

The form of solution of either equation, appropriate to the present problem, is $\xi(r, \theta) = \chi(r)\psi(\theta)$ as in §91, and the presence of the time factor $e^{i\omega t}$ is tacitly understood. Then analysis similar to that in §51 leads to the *three* ordinary D.E.

$$d^2\chi/dr^2 + d\chi/r\,dr \pm (k^2 \mp \nu^2/r^2)\chi = 0,$$

$$d^2\psi/d\theta^2 + \nu^2\psi = 0,$$

94.2

so there is one equation more than in §91 for the membrane. This addition corresponds to the $-$ sign in 94.1, and arises in virtue of the inherent stiffness (flexural rigidity) of the plate, which is absent in the membrane. The rigidity entails two more b.c. than in the case of the membrane, these being associated with bending and shear. The *four* b.c. entail a fourth order D.E. in x, y.

The first two D.E. in 94.2 have the standard forms for the ordinary and the modified Bessel equations. Their respective solutions are

$$\chi_\nu = A_\nu J_\nu(kr) + B_\nu Y_\nu(kr)$$

94.3

$$\bar\chi_\nu = C_\nu I_\nu(kr) + D_\nu K_\nu(kr),$$

94.4

and for the third equation

$$\psi_\nu = E_\nu \cos \nu\theta + F_\nu \sin \nu\theta,$$

94.5

A-F being arbitrary constants. Applying the argument below 91.6, we find that $\nu = n$, a positive integer. Hence for order n, the solution of 93.2 in polar coordinates is $(\chi_n + \bar\chi_n)\psi_n$, so

$$\xi_n(r, \theta) = \{A_n J_n(kr) + B_n Y_n(kr) + C_n I_n(kr) +$$

$$D_n K_n(kr)\}(E_n \cos n\theta + F_n \sin \theta)$$

94.6

If the plate is complete to the centre, the functions $Y_n(kr)$, $K_n(kr)$ are inadmissible in virtue of their singularities at $r = 0$. They must, of course, be retained in the case of an annular plate. Thus in the present problem $B = D = 0$, so 94.6 becomes, for modes of order $n = 0, 1, 2, \cdots$,

$$\xi_n(r, \theta) = \{A_n J_n(kr) + C_n I_n(kr)\} \cos (n\theta - \epsilon_n),$$

94.7

the constant $(E_n^2 + F_n^2)^{1/2}$ being absorbed in A_n, C_n, and $\epsilon_n =$

$\tan^{-1} F_n/E_n$ an arbitrary phase angle, which for convenience we may (on occasion) make zero. By §§91, 92, it is evident that there are n nodal diameters associated with 94.7.

95. PLATE CLAMPED AT $r = a$ The b.c. are (i) $\xi = 0$, $r = a$, (ii) $d\xi/dr = 0$, $r = a$, i.e. zero displacement and slope at the clamp. Inserting these into 94.7, and using $dJ_n(kr)/dr = kJ'_n(kr)$, $dI_n(kr)/dr = kI'_n(kr)$, where $J'_n(kr) = dJ_n(kr)/d(kr)$, yields

$$A_n J_n(ka) + C_n I_n(ka) = 0, \qquad 95.1$$

and $$k\{A_n J'_n(ka) + C_n I'_n(ka)\} = 0. \qquad 95.2$$

Eliminating A_n, C_n, leads to the frequency equation

$$J_n(ka)I'_n(ka) - J_n(ka)I'_n(ka) = 0. \qquad 95.3$$

By aid of the recurrence relations

$$J'_n = (n/ka)J_n - J_{n+1}, \qquad I'_n = (n/ka)I_n + I_{n+1}, \qquad 95.4$$

95.3 may be written, with $\lambda = ka$,

$$J_n(\lambda)I_{n+1}(\lambda) + J_{n+1}(\lambda)I_n(\lambda) = 0. \qquad 95.5$$

The roots of 95.5 are given by [1]

$$\lambda_{n,m} = k_{n,m}a \simeq w - \{(4n^2 - 1)/8w\}U(w), \qquad 95.6$$

where

$$U(w) = \left\{1 + (1/w) + \frac{28n^2 + 17}{48w^2} + \frac{3(4n^2 - 1)}{8w^3}\right.$$

$$\left. + \frac{83n^4 + 54.5n^2 + 161.19}{120w^4} + \cdots \right\},$$

with $w = (n + 2m)\pi/2$, $m \geq 1$ being the rank of the root. For given m, the accuracy of 95.6 decreases with increase in n, e.g. it is not sufficiently accurate when $m = 1$, $n = 4$.

Choosing $n = 2$, arbitrarily, the frequency equation is

$$J_2(\lambda)I_3(\lambda) + J_3(\lambda)I_2(\lambda) = 0, \qquad 95.7$$

and $\lambda_{2,1} \simeq 5.906$, $\lambda_{2,2} \simeq 9.197$, $\lambda_{2,3} \simeq 12.402$, $\lambda_{2,4} \simeq 15.579$, $\lambda_{2,5} \simeq 18.745$. As λ increases, the interval between consecutive roots tends to π, for then w is large, and 95.6 gives $\lambda_{n,m} \simeq w = (m + n/2)\pi$. Omitting the subscript 2,

$$\omega_m = ck_m^2 = (\lambda_m^2 h/a^2)\{E/12\rho(1 - \sigma^2)\}^{1/2}. \qquad 95.8$$

$k_1 a \simeq 5.906$ corresponds to the first mode, but there is no nodal circle. When $ka \simeq 9.197$, there is a nodal circle between centre and periphery, and in general corresponding to $k_m a$, there are $(m - 1)$ internal nodal circles. As stated in §96, each vibrational mode is accompanied by two nodal diameters.

96. SHAPE DURING VIBRATION; RADII OF NODAL CIRCLES.
Since ϵ_2 in 94.7 is arbitrary, we choose the value $\pi/2$, so that one of the nodal diameters is vertical (Fig. 92.1). Then the shape is given by

$$\xi_2(r, \theta) = A_2\{J_2(kr) + \varphi I_2(kr)\} \sin 2\theta, \qquad 96.1$$

where $\varphi = C_2/A_2 = -J_2(ka)/I_2(ka)$ by 95.1. When $\theta = \pi/2$, π, $3\pi/2$, 2π, $\sin 2\theta = 0$, so for these values of θ, $\xi_2 = 0$ in $0 \leq r \leq a$, and during vibration in a mode of any rank, there are two nodal diameters. As with the membrane in §92, the order of the Bessel functions determines the number of nodal diameters, while the rank of the root less 1, gives the number of internal nodal circles. The nodal patterns, in ascending order of frequency, are identical in type with those depicted in Fig. 92.1. The frequency ratios to that of the fundamental are: 2.08, 3.41; 3.88, 4.98, 5.94; 6.82, 8.26, 8.72 approximately. The second and the seventh apply in the case above. Other types of nodal figure have been obtained experimentally.[*]

When ka has one of the values λ_m, by b.c. (i) §95, $\xi_2 = 0$, so from 96.1

$$J_2(\lambda_m) + \varphi I_2(\lambda_m) = 0. \qquad 96.2$$

---

[*]R. C. Colwell and others: Philosophical Magazine, *24*, 1041, 1938; *27*, 123, 1939; Journal Acoustical Society of America *11*, 147, 1939; *12*, 260, 1940.

If R is the radius of a nodal circle, we again have $\xi_2 = 0$, so

$$J_2(k_m R) + \varphi I_2(k_m R) = 0. \qquad 96.3$$

Equating the φ from 96.2, 96.3, yields

$$J_2(k_m R)/I_2(k_m R) = J_2(\lambda_m)/I_2(\lambda_m), \qquad 96.4$$

the latter ratio being known if λ_m is assigned. Suppose that $k_m R = \mu$ satisfies this equation, then for $m \geq 2$,

$$R = \mu/k_m = \mu a/\lambda_m , \qquad 96.5$$

is the required radius. The solution of 96.4 may be effected by successive approximation using Bessel function tables.

97. EXAMPLE   Calculate the frequencies of the first three modes of a circular plate clamped at its periphery and vibrating in each mode with two nodal diameters, given that $a = 2 \times 10^{-2}$ m., $h = 10^{-4}$ m., $E = 2 \times 10^{11}$ newton per m.^{2}, $\sigma = 0.27$, $\rho = 7.7 \times 10^3$ kg. m.$^{-3}$.

By 95.8

$$\omega_1 = (\lambda_1^2 h/a^2)\{E/12\rho(1 - \sigma^2)\}^{1/2} \qquad 97.1$$

$$= \frac{5.906 \times 10^{-4}}{4 \times 10^{-4}} \left\{ \frac{2 \times 10^{11}}{12 \times 7.7 \times 10^3 \times 0.93} \right\}$$

$$\simeq 13300 \text{ radians p.s.}$$

so $\omega_1/2\pi \simeq 2120$ c.p.s.   97.2

Then

$$\omega_2/2\pi = (\omega_1/2\pi)(\lambda_2/\lambda_1)^2 \simeq 2120(9.197/5.906)^2$$

$$\simeq 5140 \text{ c.p.s.} \qquad 97.3$$

and $$\omega_3/2\pi = (\omega_1/2\pi)(\lambda_3/\lambda_1)^2 \simeq 2120(12.402/5.906)^2$$

$$\simeq 9350 \text{ c.p.s.} \qquad 97.4$$

These frequencies have the non-integral ratios $1:2.42:4.41$, so the overtones of the plate are enharmonic. If a circular gong is sounded by a striker covered with chamois leather, its tone is more mellow than that obtained using the wooden handle. In the former case the fundamental vibration predominates, the soft striker assisting the rapidity of decay of the overtones. Also the duration of contact exceeds that with the handle, thereby entailing a reduction in the high frequency end of the impulse spectrum (see §29). The aural sensation of strong enharmonic overtones is an unpleasant one.

CHAPTER X

Sound Waves of Finite Amplitude

98. INTRODUCTION For sound waves in air, the 'characteristic' is the adiabatic relationship $pv^\gamma = a$ constant, $\gamma = 1.4$. When a sound wave travels through a medium, the latter is compressed and rarefied cyclically, and the (so-called) particles move to and fro in the direction of propagation. In virtue of the non-linear relationship above, it follows that the differential equation for the propagation of sound waves will be non-linear also. To obviate this, the *classical* theory of sound is based upon infinitesimal pressure amplitude, so that the working characteristic is the tangent to the adiabatic curve at the point corresponding to the static pressure in the medium. The pressure variation, i.e. the excess pressure associated with sounds in ordinary speech, is of the order 5×10^{-2} newton. m^{-2} (0.5 dyne cm.$^{-2}$), while that due to radio, city noises, etc., is much higher. It follows, therefore, that the amplitude is far from being infinitesimal, so we live in a world of distorted sound! The distortion is still further augmented by the ear whose characteristic is non-linear and asymmetrical. However, it is only when the pressure variation exceeds 5×10^{-2} newton $m.^{-2}$, that curvature of the adiabatic characteristic need be taken into account. It must be done for sound waves of 'finite' amplitude as shown in §99 *et seq.*

99. PLANE SOUND WAVES A plane wave is a type which travels in one direction without spreading out, so the pressure variation is independent of lateral position. For instance, if a rigid disk vibrates axially at one end of a smooth uniform tube, of equal radius, filled with air, plane sound waves pass along it, provided (a) the far end of the tube is terminated by an acoustical impedance which absorbs the energy of the incident wave,

(b) there are no transverse modes of vibration within the tube.

To derive the D.E. for propagation, consider a stratum of air of undisturbed thickness dx (Fig. 99.1) in the direction of

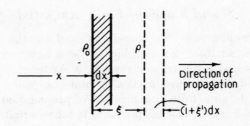

Fig. 99.1

propagation. At some instant during the passage of a sound wave, particles originally at x are at *variable* abscissa $(x + \xi)$. The thickness of the stratum is now $dx + dx\,(\partial\xi/\partial x) = (1 + \xi')\,dx$. The mass of unit area of the stratum is unchanged, so

$$\rho_0\,dx = \rho(1 + \xi')\,dx, \qquad 99.1$$

where ρ_0 is the density of the undisturbed air, and ρ that during passage of the sound wave. Thus

$$\rho/\rho_0 = 1/(1 + \xi'), \qquad 99.2$$

and

$$\partial\rho/\partial x = -\rho_0\xi''/(1 + \xi')^2 = -\rho\xi''/(1 + \xi'). \qquad 99.3$$

For adiabatic change

$$pv^\gamma = p_0 v_0^\gamma, \qquad \text{so} \qquad p = p_0(v_0/v)^\gamma = p_0(\rho/\rho_0)^\gamma, \qquad 99.4$$

and, therefore,

$$\partial p/\partial \rho = (\gamma p_0/\rho_0)(\rho/\rho_0)^{\gamma-1} = c^2/(1 + \xi')^{\gamma-1}, \qquad 99.5$$

by 99.2, where $c^2 = \gamma p_0/\rho_0$, the velocity^2 of sound waves of very small amplitude* (infinitesimal in a theoretical sense). Multiplying 99.5 by 99.3, yields

$$\partial p/\partial x = -\rho c^2 \xi''/(1 + \xi')^\gamma. \qquad 99.6$$

The pressure difference on the two sides of the stratum at $(x + \xi)$ is the product of mass per unit area given at 99.1 and acceleration, so

$$\frac{\partial p}{\partial(x + \xi)} (1 + \xi') \, dx = (\partial p/\partial x) \, dx = -\rho(1 + \xi') \, dx \, \ddot{\xi}, \qquad 99.7$$

since $\partial(x + \xi) = dx + dx \, (\partial \xi/\partial x) = (1 + \xi') \, dx$. Hence by 99.6, 99.7, we obtain the partial D.E. for the propagation of plane sound waves of finite amplitude, namely

$$\xi'' = (1 + \xi')^{\gamma+1} \ddot{\xi}/c^2, \qquad 99.8$$

which is non-linear, because ξ on the r.h.s. occurs to a power higher than unity. When the amplitude is small enough, $\xi' \ll 1$, and 99.8 degenerates to the well-known linear classical form

$$\xi'' = \ddot{\xi}/c^2, \qquad 99.9$$

which is identical in type with the D.E. at 51.5, 61.3, 70.4, 73.3, for a transversely vibrating string, longitudinal vibration of a bar (sound waves therein), longitudinal vibration of a coil spring, and torsional vibration of a bar, respectively. The general solution of 99.9 is 54.1, and the remarks in the first paragraph of §54 apply here also.

100. SOLUTION OF 99.8: FIRST APPROXIMATION   The method used is one of successive approximation (iteration) in which a *linear* partial D.E. is solved at each stage. If $\xi' \ll 1$,

$$(1 + \xi')^{\gamma+1} = 1 + (\gamma + 1)\xi' + (\gamma + 1)\gamma \xi'^2/2 + \cdots \qquad 100.1$$

$$\simeq 1 + (\gamma + 1)\xi'. \qquad 100.2$$

---

*In a sound wave of finite amplitude, the crests of the waves travel faster than the troughs, so the former gain on the latter and distortion of waveform results. The points of zero excess pressure travel with velocity c. The theory does not hold for very large pressure amplitude.

Substituting this into 99.8 gives the approximate D.E.

$$\xi'' - \ddot{\xi}/c^2 = (\gamma + 1)\xi'\ddot{\xi}/c^2, \qquad 100.3$$

non-linear in ξ, due to the product $\xi'\ddot{\xi}$, which is of order ξ^2. We may suppose that the motion at $x = 0$ (any suitable origin) is represented by $\xi = \xi_0 \cos \omega t$, and for a first approximation we neglect the r.h.s. of 100.3, since $\xi' \ll 1$. Then we have to solve the *linear* partial D.E.

$$\xi'' - \ddot{\xi}/c^2 = 0, \qquad 100.4$$

i.e. 99.9.

Assume a solution of the form

$$Re \ \{\psi(x)e^{i\omega t}\}, \qquad 100.5$$

where Re denotes the real part. Substituting into 100.4 gives

$$d^2\psi/dx^2 + k^2\psi = 0, \qquad 100.6$$

where $k = \omega/c = 2\pi/\lambda$ having dimension l^{-1}, λ being the wavelength. The complete solution of 100.6 is

$$\psi = Ae^{-ikx} + Be^{ikx}. \qquad 100.7$$

Since the transmission is in the positive direction of x, the B term is inapplicable (it applies in the direction x decreasing), so

$$\xi_1 = Re \ \{Ae^{i(\omega t - kx)}\}. \qquad 100.8$$

If we take $A = \xi_0$, then

$$\xi_1 = \xi_0 \cos (\omega t - kx), \qquad 100.9$$

and the condition at $x = 0$, is satisfied. This first approximation is valid for very small amplitudes, and is *a* solution of the linear D.E. 99.9.

101. SECOND APPROXIMATION   We now substitute 100.9 into the r.h.s. of 100.3. Taking $\theta = (\omega t - kx)$, we get

$$\xi' = \xi_0 k \sin \theta, \qquad \ddot{\xi} = -\xi_0\omega^2 \cos \theta, \qquad 101.1$$

so $$(\gamma + 1)\xi'\ddot{\xi}/c^2 = -\{(\gamma + 1)/2\}\xi_0^2 k^3 \sin 2\theta, \qquad 101.2$$

and 100.3 becomes

$$\xi'' - \ddot{\xi}/c^2 = -\{(\gamma + 1)/2\}\xi_0^2 k^3 \sin 2\theta. \qquad 101.3$$

The particular integral of 101.3 is

$$\xi_2 = -\{(\gamma + 1)/8\}\xi_0^2 k^2 x \cos 2\theta. \qquad 101.4$$

The complete solution of 101.3 *for the second harmonic*, is 101.4 plus the complementary function, such that the whole vanishes at $x = 0$ for $t \geq 0$, since the condition at the origin is $\xi = \xi_0 \cos \omega t$. The c.f. for outgoing waves is

$$\xi_{2c} = A_2 \cos 2\theta, \qquad 101.5$$

so we must have $A_2 = 0$. Then the periodic part of the solution, to the second order in ξ, is the sum of 100.9 and 101.4, so

$$\xi = \xi_1 + \xi_2 = \text{fundamental} + \text{second harmonic}$$

$$101.6$$

$$= \xi_0 \cos \theta - \{(\gamma + 1)/8\}\xi_0^2 k^2 x \cos 2\theta.$$

If the above procedure is repeated, the periodic part of the solution to the third order in ξ, is

$$\xi = \xi_0\{1 - (\gamma + 1)^2\xi_0^2 k^4 x^2/32\} \cos \theta$$

$$- \{(\gamma + 1)\xi_0^3 k^3 x/16\} \sin \theta$$

$$- \{(\gamma + 1)\xi_0^2 k^2 x/8\} \cos 2\theta \qquad 101.7$$

$$+ \{(\gamma + 1)^2\xi_0^3 k^4 x^2/32\} \cos 3\theta$$

$$- \{\gamma(\gamma + 1)\xi_0^3 k^3 x/48\} \sin 3\theta.$$

In 101.6, 101.7, the amplitude of the second harmonic increases linearly with increase in x, although this might not be the case if a higher approximation were taken. In virtue of the approximate nature of the solution, these formulae cease to apply when $x >$ some value x_0. Stipulating that $|\xi_2| \leq 1/4 |\xi_1|$, by 101.6 we get the restriction $(\gamma + 1)\xi_0 k^2 x/2 \leq 1$. As the sound waves travel onwards, energy is transferred from the fundamental to the harmonics, which is evident from the reduction of the former in 101.7 as x increases, $0 < x \leq x_0$. The sum of the energy in the fundamental and the infinity of harmonics at any x in $0 < x \leq x_0$, is equal to that in the fundamental at $x = 0$.

102. NON-PERIODIC COMPLEMENTARY FUNCTION OF 101.3 Cx is a c.f. of 100.4 and 101.3 which vanishes at $x = 0$ for $t > 0$. Since no initial conditions were specified in dealing with steady vibrations, C is an arbitrary constant, so in this respect the solution is indeterminate. As we are concerned solely with periodic motion, the indeterminateness is inconsequential, so we may put $C = 0$.

Unidirectional sound propagation in a long uniform tube is a degenerate case of that in a long exponential horn [15] whose cross-sectional area is $A = A_0 e^{2\beta x}$. As $\beta \to 0$, the value of C for this case degenerates to $(\gamma - 1)\xi_0^2 k^2/4$ for a tube. The presence of the term $(\gamma - 1)\xi_0^2 k^2 x/4$ in 101.6 would imply a unidirectional displacement, or in radio terminology, a rectification effect. It is due to the adiabatic curve being asymmetrical about the static point $(p_0 v_0)$. This usually gives rise to a second harmonic, while the 'centre of oscillation' moves *down* the characteristic. The latter effect may be explained as follows. The excess pressure at *variable* abscissa $(x + \xi)$ is approximately [10]

$$p = -\rho_0 c^2 \xi'. \qquad 102.1$$

Thus for the term $(\gamma - 1)\xi_0^2 k^2 x/4$, p is negative as required. It appears that the unidirectional displacement increases indefinitely with increase in x, but if the restriction on x in §101 is used, this does not happen.

★103. FREQUENCY INTERMODULATION In §41 it was shown that when two forces of different frequencies were applied to a system having a non-linear characteristic, this effect occurred. Consequently we should expect it to happen when two plane sound waves of *finite* amplitude, but different frequencies, are transmitted through air. If the displacement at $x = 0$ is given by

$$\xi = \xi_1 \cos \omega_1 t + \xi_2 \cos \omega_2 t, \qquad 103.1$$

analysis on the lines of previous sections yields, to the second order in ξ, the result

$$\xi = \xi_1 \cos \theta_1 + \xi_2 \cos \theta_2 - \{(\gamma + 1)x/8\} \{\xi_1^2 k_1^2 \cos 2\theta_1$$

$$+ \xi_2^2 k_2^2 \cos 2\theta_2 + 2\xi_1\xi_2 k_1 k_2 \cos (\theta_1 + \theta_2) \qquad 103.2$$

$$- 2\xi_1\xi_2 k_1 k_2 \cos (\theta_1 - \theta_2)\},$$

where $k_m = \omega_m/c$, $\theta_m = (\omega_m t - k_m x)$. The intermodulation is represented by the sum and difference frequencies. From this we infer that if ω_1, ω_2 were supersonic, but $(\omega_1 - \omega_2)$ in the audio range, the difference tone should be audible, provided $2\xi_1\xi_2 k_1 k_2$ were large enough.

★104. LONGITUDINAL WAVES IN UNIFORM RUBBER ROD   In [7] the D.E. for finite amplitude is shown to be

$$\xi'' = (3/c^2)\xi\{(1 + \xi')^3/[2 + (1 + \xi')^3]\}, \qquad 104.1$$

where $c^2 = E/\rho$. If the transmission is unidirectional, and $\xi = \xi_0 \cos \omega t$ at $x = 0$, to the second order in ξ the periodic part of the displacement is given by

$$\xi = \xi_0 \cos \theta - (\xi_0^2 k^2 x/4) \cos 2\theta. \qquad 104.2$$

As in §102, there is a c.f. Cx, independent of t, which vanishes at $x = 0$, C being arbitrary unless initial conditions are specified. This indicates a unidirectional displacement which increases linearly with x. 104.2 is valid if $| \xi_2 | \leq 1/4 | \xi_1 |$, i.e. $\xi_0 k^2 x \leq 1$, so there would be a restriction on this displacement. Excluding non-periodic terms, to the third order in ξ, the solution of 104.1 is

$$\xi = \xi_0(1 - \xi_0^2 k^4 x^2/8) \cos \theta - (\xi_0^3 k^3 x/8) \sin \theta$$

$$- (\xi_0^2 k^2 x/4) \cos 2\theta + (\xi_0^3 k^4 x^2/8) \cos 3\theta \qquad 104.3$$

$$- (\xi_0^3 k^3 x/24) \sin 3\theta.$$

References

1. Airey, J. R. Proc. Phys. Soc. London, *23*, 225, 1911.
2. Carrier, G. F. Quart. Appl. Math., *3*, 157, 1945.
3. Churchill, R. V. *Modern Operational Methods in Engineering* (1944).
4. Churchill, R. V. *Complex Variables and Applications* (1948).
5. Den Hartog, J. P. *Mechanical Vibrations*, 3rd edition (1947).
6. Friedrichs, K. O., and Stoker, J. J. Quart. Appl. Math., *1*, 97, 1943.
7. James, H. M., and Guth, E. Jour. Appl. Physics, *16*, 643, 1945:
8. Ludeke, C. A. Jour. Appl. Physics, (a) *17*, 603, 1946; (b) *20*, 600, 1949.
9. Ludeke, C. A. Amer. Jour. Physics, *16*, 430, 1948.
10. McLachlan, N. W. *Loudspeakers* (1934).
11. McLachlan, N. W. *Bessel Functions for Engineers* (1946).
12. McLachlan, N. W. *Complex Variable and Operational Calculus* (1942).
13. McLachlan, N. W. *Modern Operational Calculus* (1948).
14. McLachlan, N. W. *Theory and Application of Mathieu Functions* (1947).
15. McLachlan, N. W. *Ordinary Non-linear Differential Equations* (1950).
16. Minorsky, N. *Introduction to Non-linear Mechanics* (1947).
17. Ormondroyd, J., and Den Hartog, J. P. Trans. Amer. Soc. Mech. Engrs., *50*, 9, 1928.
18. Pipes, L. A. *Applied Mathematics for Engineers and Physicists* (1946).
19. Rayleigh, Lord. *Theory of Sound*, Edited by R. B. Lindsay (1945).
20. Southwell, R. V. *Introduction to Theory of Elasticity* (1941).
21. Thomson, W. T. Jour. Acous. Soc. Amer., *21*, 34, 1949.
22. Timoshenko, S. *Vibration Problems in Engineering*, 2nd edition (1937).

*Index**